## Changes

# Up and Down
# the Number Line

### Grade 3

*Also appropriate for Grade 4*

Cornelia C. Tierney
Amy Shulman Weinberg
Ricardo Nemirovsky

D1473548

*Developed at TERC, Cambridge, Massachusetts*

Scott
Foresman

**Editorial Offices:** Glenview, Illinois • Parsippany, New Jersey • New York, New York
**Sales Offices:** Parsippany, New Jersey • Duluth, Georgia • Glenview, Illinois
Coppell, Texas • Ontario, California

**http://www.scottforesman.com**

This project was supported, in part,
by the
**National Science Foundation**
Opinions expressed are those of the authors
and not necessarily those of the Foundation

TERC

The *Investigations* curriculum was developed at TERC (formerly Technical Education Research Centers) in collaboration with Kent State University and the State University of New York at Buffalo. The work was supported in part by National Science Foundation Grant No. ESI-9050210. TERC is a nonprofit company working to improve mathematics and science education. TERC is located at 2067 Massachusetts Avenue, Cambridge, MA 02140.

Managing Editor: Catherine Anderson
Series Editor: Beverly Cory
Revision Team: Laura Marshall Alavosus, Ellen Harding, Patty Green Holubar, Suzanne Knott, Beverly Hersh Lozoff
ESL Consultant: Nancy Sokol Green
Production/Manufacturing Director: Janet Yearian
Production/Manufacturing Coordinator: Amy Changar, Shannon Miller
Design Manager: Jeff Kelly
Design: Don Taka
Illustrations: DJ Simison, Carl Yoshihara
Cover: Bay Graphics
Composition: Archetype Book Composition

ISBN 0-201-37826-4
This product may appear as part of package ISBN 0-201-37801-9.
4 5 6 7 8 9 10-VO31-08 07 06 05

**INVESTIGATIONS IN NUMBER, DATA, AND SPACE®**

T E R C

*Principal Investigator*    Susan Jo Russell

*Co-Principal Investigator*    Cornelia C. Tierney

*Director of Research and Evaluation*    Jan Mokros

*Curriculum Development*
Joan Akers
Michael T. Battista
Mary Berle-Carman
Douglas H. Clements
Karen Economopoulos
Ricardo Nemirovsky
Andee Rubin
Susan Jo Russell
Cornelia C. Tierney
Amy Shulman Weinberg

*Evaluation and Assessment*
Mary Berle-Carman
Abouali Farmanfarmaian
Jan Mokros
Mark Ogonowski
Amy Shulman Weinberg
Tracey Wright
Lisa Yaffee

*Teacher Support*
Rebecca B. Corwin
Karen Economopoulos
Tracey Wright
Lisa Yaffee

*Technology Development*
Michael T. Battista
Douglas H. Clements
Julie Sarama Meredith
Andee Rubin

*Video Production*
David A. Smith

*Administration and Production*
Amy Catlin
Amy Taber

*Cooperating Classrooms
for This Unit*
Katie Bloomfield
Robert A. Dihlmann
Shutesbury Elementary
Shutesbury, MA

Joan Forsyth
Jeanne Wall
Arlington Public Schools
Arlington, MA

Helen McElroy
Cambridge Friends School
Cambridge, MA

Angela Philactos
Judy Weisenberger
Boston Public Schools
Boston, MA

*Consultants and Advisors*
Elizabeth Badger
Deborah Lowenberg Ball
Marilyn Burns
Ann Grady
Joanne M. Gurry
James J. Kaput
Steven Leinwand
Mary M. Lindquist
David S. Moore
John Olive
Leslie P. Steffe
Peter Sullivan
Grayson Wheatley
Virginia Woolley
Anne Zarinnia

*Graduate Assistants*
*Kent State University*
Joanne Caniglia
Pam DeLong
Carol King

*State University of New York at Buffalo*
Rosa Gonzalez
Sue McMillen
Julie Sarama Meredith
Sudha Swaminathan

*Revisions and Home Materials*
Cathy Miles Grant
Marlene Kliman
Margaret McGaffigan
Megan Murray
Kim O'Neil
Andee Rubin
Susan Jo Russell
Lisa Seyferth
Myriam Steinback
Judy Storeygard
Anna Suarez
Cornelia Tierney
Carol Walker
Tracey Wright

# CONTENTS

## TEACHER NOTES

## WHERE TO START

The first-time user of *Up and Down the Number Line* should read the following:

When you next teach this same unit, you can begin to read more of the background. Each time you present the unit, you will learn more about how your students understand the mathematical ideas.

*Investigations in Number, Data, and Space*® is a K–5 mathematics curriculum with four major goals:

- to offer students meaningful mathematical problems
- to emphasize depth in mathematical thinking rather than superficial exposure to a series of fragmented topics
- to communicate mathematics content and pedagogy to teachers
- to substantially expand the pool of mathematically literate students

The *Investigations* curriculum embodies a new approach based on years of research about how children learn mathematics. Each grade level consists of a set of separate units, each offering 2–8 weeks of work. These units of study are presented through investigations that involve students in the exploration of major mathematical ideas.

Approaching the mathematics content through investigations helps students develop flexibility and confidence in approaching problems, fluency in using mathematical skills and tools to solve problems, and proficiency in evaluating their solutions. Students also build a repertoire of ways to communicate about their mathematical thinking, while their enjoyment and appreciation of mathematics grows.

The investigations are carefully designed to invite all students into mathematics—girls and boys, members of diverse cultural, ethnic, and language groups, and students with different strengths and interests. Problem contexts often call on students to share experiences from their family, culture, or community. The curriculum eliminates barriers—such as work in isolation from peers, or emphasis on speed and memorization—that exclude some students from participating successfully in mathematics. The following aspects of the curriculum ensure that all students are included in significant mathematics learning:

- Students spend time exploring problems in depth.
- They find more than one solution to many of the problems they work on.

- They invent their own strategies and approaches, rather than relying on memorized procedures.
- They choose from a variety of concrete materials and appropriate technology, including calculators, as a natural part of their everyday mathematical work.
- They express their mathematical thinking through drawing, writing, and talking.
- They work in a variety of groupings—as a whole class, individually, in pairs, and in small groups.
- They move around the classroom as they explore the mathematics in their environment and talk with their peers.

While reading and other language activities are typically given a great deal of time and emphasis in elementary classrooms, mathematics often does not get the time it needs. If students are to experience mathematics in depth, they must have enough time to become engaged in real mathematical problems. We believe that a minimum of five hours of mathematics classroom time a week—about an hour a day—is critical at the elementary level. The plan and pacing of the *Investigations* curriculum are based on that belief.

We explain more about the pedagogy and principles that underlie these investigations in Teacher Notes throughout the units. For correlations of the curriculum to the NCTM Standards and further help in using this research-based program for teaching mathematics, see the following books:

- *Implementing the* Investigations in Number, Data, and Space® *Curriculum*
- *Beyond Arithmetic: Changing Mathematics in the Elementary Classroom* by Jan Mokros, Susan Jo Russell, and Karen Economopoulos

This book is one of the curriculum units for *Investigations in Number, Data, and Space.* In addition to providing part of a complete mathematics curriculum for your students, this unit offers information to support your own professional development. You, the teacher, are the person who will make this curriculum come alive in the classroom; the book for each unit is your main support system.

Although the curriculum does not include student textbooks, reproducible sheets for student work are provided in the unit and are also available as Student Activity Booklets. Students work actively with objects and experiences in their own environment and with a variety of manipulative materials and technology, rather than with a book of instruction and problems. We strongly recommend use of the overhead projector as a way to present problems, to focus group discussion, and to help students share ideas and strategies.

Ultimately, every teacher will use these investigations in ways that make sense for his or her particular style, the particular group of students, and the constraints and supports of a particular school environment. Each unit offers information and

guidance for a wide variety of situations, drawn from our collaborations with many teachers and students over many years. Our goal in this book is to help you, a professional educator, implement this curriculum in a way that will give all your students access to mathematical power.

### Investigation Format

The opening two pages of each investigation help you get ready for the work that follows.

**What Happens** This gives a synopsis of each session or block of sessions.

**Mathematical Emphasis** This lists the most important ideas and processes students will encounter in this investigation.

**What to Plan Ahead of Time** These lists alert you to materials to gather, sheets to duplicate, transparencies to make, and anything else you need to do before starting.

**Sessions** Within an investigation, the activities are organized by class session, a session being at least a one-hour math class. Sessions are numbered consecutively through an investigation. Often sev-

---

# Net Change

### What Happens

**Sessions 1 and 2: Elevator Trips Up and Down** Students plan the layout of a fantasy skyscraper for children and prepare their own skyscraper diagrams and changes cards. They choose a starting floor and an ending floor and figure out the net change (how far and in what direction they have moved).

**Sessions 3 and 4: Many Ways to Make One Net Change** Students find many sets of changes that make the same net change. They play a game in which they use as many changes as they can to make a given net change.

**Session 5: Thirty Changes** Students post a sequence of 30 changes along a wall. Working in groups, they find out what the total or net effect of applying all the changes would be. They use strategies they have learned, such as –2 cancels +2, so if they count three –2's and five +2's, they know they need to consider only the extra two +2's.

**Sessions 6 and 7: Missing Information Problems** Students solve changes problems in which critical information is missing: either the starting point or one or more of the changes. They write about their strategies for finding a missing starting floor.

**Session 8 (Excursion): Stopping at Many Floors** Students play a game in which they arrange a set of changes to make the elevator stop on as many different floors as they can.

### Mathematical Emphasis

- Developing the concept of net change, which specifies both how far and in which direction (positive or negative) an object has moved in all after a series of moves in each direction
- Developing strategies for computing net change and for using net change to find a missing end point or starting point
- Recognizing that net change is the same regardless of the order in which changes are carried out
- Using a change in the negative direction to cancel a change in the positive direction
- Developing strategies for adding a long sequence of changes, including the use of a calculator
- Constructing different sequences of positive and negative numbers to produce the same net change

---

### What to Plan Ahead of Time

**Materials**

- Chart paper (Sessions 1–4)
- Stick-on notes, 1½" × 2" or a bit larger: 2 pads (Sessions 1–7)
- Chips, cubes, or other small objects to use as game pieces: 10 per student (Sessions 1–4, 6–8)
- Quart-size resealable plastic bags for holding materials: 1 per student (Sessions 1–4, 6–8)
- Scissors: 1 per student (Sessions 1–4)
- Tape for assembling skyscrapers (Sessions 1–2)
- Paper clips: 1 per student (Sessions 3–4)
- Crayons, colored pencils, or markers (Sessions 3–4)
- Paper and pencils (Session 8)
- Calculators: 1 per student (Sessions 3–5)
- Overhead projector (Sessions 1–4)

**Other Preparation**

- Duplicate student sheets and teaching resources (located at the end of this unit) in the following quantities. If you have Student Activity Booklets, copy only the items marked with an asterisk, including any transparencies and extra materials needed.

  *For Sessions 1–2*
  Student Sheet 1, Net Change from Start to Finish (p. 61): 2 per student (1 for homework)
  Skyscraper (p. 70): 2 per student (1 for homework), and 1 transparency*
  Family letter* (p. 60): 1 per student. Remember to sign it before copying.

  *For Sessions 3–4*
  Student Sheet 2, Net Change with Many Changes (p. 62): 2 per student (1 for homework)

  Changes Cards (p. 89): 2 sets per student (1 for homework)
  Net Change Cards (p. 71): 1 set per student
  Student Sheet 3, How to Play the Game of Many Changes (p. 63): 1 per student
  Student Sheet 4, Many Changes to Make +2 (p. 64): 1 per student

  *For Session 5*
  Student Sheet 5, Mixed-Up Changes (p. 65): 1 per student (homework)

  *For Sessions 6–7*
  Student Sheet 6, Missing Information Problems (p. 66): 1 per student, plus some extras*
  Student Sheet 7, Six Changes and a Missing Start (p. 67): 1 per student

  *For Session 8*
  Student Sheet 8, Pick Up Chips (p. 68): 1 per pair or group (class), 1 per student (homework), and 1 transparency*
  Student Sheet 9, How to Play Pick Up Chips (p. 69): 1 per student (homework)

- Assemble one skyscraper as an example. Or, to save time, assemble skyscrapers for all students. (Session 1, optional)
- Cut small stick-on note pads in half, with sticky backing on each piece, making a mini-pad of 8–10 notes for each student.
- Try all the games yourself or with a few students before you play them with the whole class. (Sessions 3–4, 8)
- If you plan to provide folders in which students will save their work for the entire unit, prepare these for distribution during Session 1.

---

eral sessions are grouped together, presenting a block of activities with a single major focus.

When you find a block of sessions presented together—for example, Sessions 1, 2, and 3—read through the entire block first to understand the overall flow and sequence of the activities. Make some preliminary decisions about how you will divide the activities into three sessions for your class, based on what you know about your students. You may need to modify your initial plans as you progress through the activities, and you may want to make notes in the margins of the pages as reminders for the next time you use the unit.

Be sure to read the Session Follow-Up section at the end of the session block to see what homework assignments and extensions are suggested as you make your initial plans.

While you may be used to a curriculum that tells you exactly what each class session should cover, we have found that the teacher is in a better position to make these decisions. Each unit is flexible and may be handled somewhat differently by every teacher. While we provide guidance for how many sessions a particular group of activities is likely to need, we want you to be active in determining an appropriate pace and the best transition points for your class. It is not unusual for a teacher to spend more or less time than is proposed for the activities.

**Ten-Minute Math** At the beginning of some sessions, you will find Ten-Minute Math activities. These are designed to be used in tandem with the investigations, but not during the math hour. Rather, we hope you will do them whenever you have a spare 10 minutes—maybe before lunch or recess, or at the end of the day.

Ten-Minute Math offers practice in key concepts, but not always those being covered in the unit. For example, in a unit on using data, Ten-Minute Math might revisit geometric activities done earlier in the year. Complete directions for the suggested activities are included at the end of each unit.

**Activities** The activities include pair and small-group work, individual tasks, and whole-class discussions. In any case, students are seated together, talking and sharing ideas during all work times. Students most often work cooperatively, although each student may record work individually.

**Choice Time** In some units, some sessions are structured with activity choices. In these cases, students may work simultaneously on different activities focused on the same mathematical ideas. Students choose which activities they want to do, and they cycle through them.

You will need to decide how to set up and introduce these activities and how to let students make their choices. Some teachers present them as station activities, in different parts of the room. Some list the choices on the board as reminders or have students keep their own lists.

**Extensions** Sometimes in Session Follow-Up, you will find suggested extension activities. These are opportunities for some or all students to explore a topic in greater depth or in a different context. They are not designed for "fast" students; mathematics is a multifaceted discipline, and different students will want to go further in different investigations. Look for and encourage the sparks of interest and enthusiasm you see in your students, and use the extensions to help them pursue these interests.

**Excursions** Some of the *Investigations* units include excursions—blocks of activities that could be omitted without harming the integrity of the unit. This is one way of dealing with the great depth and variety of elementary mathematics—much more than a class has time to explore in any one year. Excursions give you the flexibility to make different choices from year to year, doing the excursion in one unit this time, and next year trying another excursion.

**Tips for the Linguistically Diverse Classroom** At strategic points in each unit, you will find concrete suggestions for simple modifications of the teaching strategies to encourage the participation of all students. Many of these tips offer alternative ways to elicit critical thinking from students at varying levels of English proficiency, as well as from other students who find it difficult to verbalize their thinking.

The tips are supported by suggestions for specific vocabulary work to help ensure that all students can participate fully in the investigations. The Preview for the Linguistically Diverse Classroom (p. I-19) lists important words that are assumed as part of the working vocabulary of the unit. Second-language learners will need to become familiar with these words in order to understand the problems and activities they will be doing. These terms can be incorporated into students' second-language work before or during the unit. Activities that can be used to present the words are found in the appendix, Vocabulary Support for Second-Language Learners (p. 57). In addition, ideas for making connections to students' language and cultures, included on the Preview page, help the class explore the unit's concepts from a multicultural perspective.

## Materials

A complete list of the materials needed for teaching this unit is found on p. I-16. Some of these materials are available in kits for the *Investigations* curriculum. Individual items can also be purchased from school supply dealers.

**Classroom Materials** In an active mathematics classroom, certain basic materials should be available at all times: interlocking cubes, pencils, unlined paper, graph paper, calculators, things to count with, and measuring tools. Some activities in this curriculum require scissors and glue sticks or tape. Stick-on notes and large paper are also useful materials throughout.

So that students can independently get what they need at any time, they should know where these materials are kept, how they are stored, and how they are to be returned to the storage area. For example, interlocking cubes are best stored in towers of ten; then, whatever the activity, they should be returned to storage in groups of ten at the end of the hour. You'll find that establishing such routines at the beginning of the year is well worth the time and effort.

**Technology** Calculators are used throughout *Investigations*. Many of the units recommend that you have at least one calculator for each pair. You will find calculator activities, plus Teacher Notes discussing this important mathematical tool, in an early unit at each grade level. It is assumed that calculators will be readily available for student use.

Computer activities at grade 3 use two software programs that were developed especially for the *Investigations* curriculum. *Tumbling Tetrominoes* is introduced in the 2-D Geometry unit, *Flips, Turns, and Area.* This game emphasizes ideas

about area and about geometric motions (slides, flips, and turns). The program *Geo-Logo*™ is introduced in a second 2-D Geometry unit, *Turtle Paths,* where students use it to explore geometric shapes.

How you use the computer activities depends on the number of computers you have available. Suggestions are offered in the geometry units for how to organize different types of computer environments.

**Children's Literature** Each unit offers a list of suggested children's literature (p. I-16) that can be used to support the mathematical ideas in the unit. Sometimes an activity is based on a specific children's book, with suggestions for substitutions where practical. While such activities can be adapted and taught without the book, the literature offers a rich introduction and should be used whenever possible.

**Student Sheets and Teaching Resources** Student recording sheets and other teaching tools needed for both class and homework are provided as reproducible blackline masters at the end of each unit. They are also available as Student Activity Booklets. These booklets contain all the sheets each student will need for individual work, freeing you from extensive copying (although you may need or want to copy the occasional teaching resource on transparency film or card stock, or make extra copies of a student sheet).

We think it's important that students find their own ways of organizing and recording their work. They need to learn how to explain their thinking with both drawings and written words, and how to organize their results so someone else can understand them. For this reason, we deliberately do not provide student sheets for every activity. Regardless of the form in which students do their work, we recommend that they keep a mathematics notebook or folder so that their work is always available for reference.

**Assessment Sourcebook** The *Assessment Sourcebook* provides sets of End-of-Unit Assessment Tasks and Assessment Masters designed to assess students' understanding of the most important mathematical ideas of the unit. The

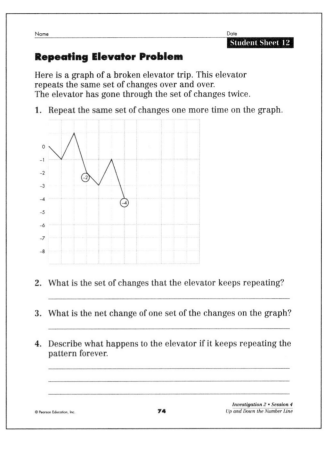

*Sourcebook* also provides information about the mathematical significance of each assessment task; suggestions on how to observe students and evaluate their work; and unit checklists of mathematical emphases. Each checklist provides space to make short notes about individual students.

**Homework** In *Investigations,* homework is an extension of classroom work. Sometimes it offers review and practice of work done in class, sometimes preparation for upcoming activities, and sometimes numerical practice that revisits work in earlier units. Homework plays a role both in supporting students' learning and in helping inform families about the ways in which students in this curriculum work with mathematical ideas.

Depending on your school's homework policies and your own judgment, you may want to assign more homework than is suggested in the units. For this purpose you might use the practice pages, included as blackline masters at the end of this unit, to give students additional work with numbers.

For some homework assignments, you will want to adapt the activity to meet the needs of a variety of students in your class: those with special needs, those ready for more challenge, and second-language learners. You might change the numbers in a problem, make the activity more or less complex, or go through a sample activity with those who need extra help. You can modify any student sheet for either homework or class use. In particular, making numbers in a problem smaller or larger can make the same basic activity appropriate for a wider range of students.

Another issue to consider is how to handle the homework that students bring back to class—how to recognize the work they have done at home without spending too much time on it. Some teachers hold a short group discussion of different approaches to the assignment; others ask students to share and discuss their work with a neighbor, or post the homework around the room and give students time to tour it briefly. If you want to keep track of homework students bring in, be sure it ends up in a designated place.

*Investigations* at Home  It is a good idea to make your policy on homework explicit to both students and their families when you begin teaching with *Investigations*. How frequently will you be assigning homework? When do you expect homework to be completed and brought back to school? What are your goals in assigning homework? How independent should families expect their children to be? What should the parent's or guardian's role be? The more explicit you can be about your expectations, the better the homework experience will be for everyone.

*Investigations* at Home (a booklet available separately for each unit, to send home with students) gives you a way to communicate with families about the work students are doing in class. This booklet includes a brief description of every session, a list of the mathematics content emphasized in each investigation, and a discussion of each homework assignment to help families more effectively support their children. Whether or not you are using the *Investigations* at Home booklets, we expect you to make your own choices about home-

work assignments. Feel free to omit any and to add extra ones you think are appropriate.

**Family Letter**  A letter that you can send home to students' families is included with the blackline masters for each unit. Families need to be informed about the mathematics work in your classroom; they should be encouraged to participate in and support their children's work. A reminder to send home the letter for each unit appears in one of the early investigations. These letters are also available separately in Spanish, Vietnamese, Cantonese, Hmong, and Cambodian.

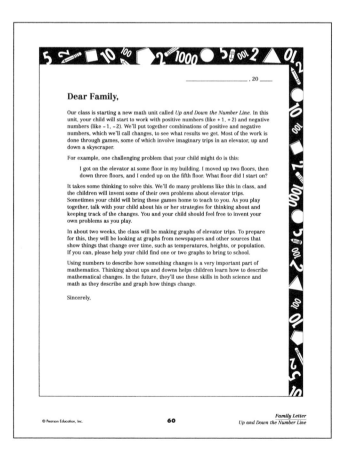

## Help for You, the Teacher

Because we believe strongly that a new curriculum must help teachers think in new ways about mathematics and about their students' mathematical thinking processes, we have included a great deal of material to help you learn more about both.

**About the Mathematics in This Unit** This introductory section (p. I-17) summarizes the critical information about the mathematics you will be teaching. It describes the unit's central mathematical ideas and how students will encounter them through the unit's activities.

**Teacher Notes** These reference notes provide practical information about the mathematics you are teaching and about our experience with how students learn. Many of the notes were written in response to actual questions from teachers, or to discuss important things we saw happening in the field-test classrooms. Some teachers like to read them all before starting the unit, then review them as they come up in particular investigations.

**Dialogue Boxes** Sample dialogues demonstrate how students typically express their mathematical ideas, what issues and confusions arise in their thinking, and how some teachers have guided class discussions.

These dialogues are based on the extensive classroom testing of this curriculum; many are word-for-word transcriptions of recorded class discussions. They are not always easy reading; sometimes it may take some effort to unravel what the students are trying to say. But this is the value of these dialogues; they offer good clues to how your students may develop and express their approaches and strategies, helping you prepare for your own class discussions.

**Where to Start** You may not have time to read everything the first time you use this unit. As a first-time user, you will likely focus on understanding the activities and working them out with your students. Read completely through each investigation before starting to present it. Also read those sections listed in the Contents under the heading Where to Start (p. vi).

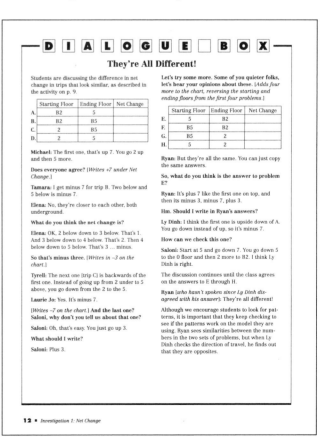

The *Investigations* curriculum incorporates the use of two forms of technology in the classroom: calculators and computers. Calculators are assumed to be standard classroom materials, available for student use in any unit. Computers are explicitly linked to one or more units at each grade level; they are used with the unit on 2-D geometry at each grade, as well as with some of the units on measuring, data, and changes.

## Using Calculators

In this curriculum, calculators are considered tools for doing mathematics, similar to pattern blocks or interlocking cubes. Just as with other tools, students must learn both *how* to use calculators correctly and *when* they are appropriate to use. This knowledge is crucial for daily life, as calculators are now a standard way of handling numerical operations, both at work and at home.

Using a calculator correctly is not a simple task; it depends on a good knowledge of the four operations and of the number system, so that students can select suitable calculations and also determine what a reasonable result would be. These skills are the basis of any work with numbers, whether or not a calculator is involved.

Unfortunately, calculators are often seen as tools to check computations with, as if other methods are somehow more fallible. Students need to understand that any computational method can be used to check any other; it's just as easy to make a mistake on the calculator as it is to make a mistake on paper or with mental arithmetic. Throughout this curriculum, we encourage students to solve computation problems in more than one way in order to double-check their accuracy. We present mental arithmetic, paper-and-pencil computation, and calculators as three possible approaches.

In this curriculum we also recognize that, despite their importance, calculators are not always appropriate in mathematics instruction. Like any tools, calculators are useful for some tasks, but not for others. You will need to make decisions about when to allow students access to calculators and when to ask that they solve problems without them, so that they can concentrate on other tools and skills. At times when calculators are or are not appropriate for a particular activity, we make specific recommendations. Help your students develop their own sense of which problems they can tackle with their own reasoning and which ones might be better solved with a combination of their own reasoning and the calculator.

Managing calculators in your classroom so that they are a tool, and not a distraction, requires some planning. When calculators are first introduced, students often want to use them for everything, even problems that can be solved quite simply by other methods. However, once the novelty wears off, students are just as interested in developing their own strategies, especially when these strategies are emphasized and valued in the classroom. Over time, students will come to recognize the ease and value of solving problems mentally, with paper and pencil, or with manipulatives, while also understanding the power of the calculator to facilitate work with larger numbers.

Experience shows that if calculators are available only occasionally, students become excited and distracted when they are permitted to use them. They focus on the tool rather than on the mathematics. In order to learn when calculators are appropriate and when they are not, students must have easy access to them and use them routinely in their work.

If you have a calculator for each student, and if you think your students can accept the responsibility, you might allow them to keep their calculators with the rest of their individual materials, at least for the first few weeks of school. Alternatively, you might store them in boxes on a shelf, number each calculator, and assign a corresponding number to each student. This system can give students a sense of ownership while also helping you keep track of the calculators.

## Using Computers

Students can use computers to approach and visualize mathematical situations in new ways. The computer allows students to construct and manipulate geometric shapes, see objects move according to rules they specify, and turn, flip, and repeat a pattern.

This curriculum calls for computers in units where they are a particularly effective tool for learning mathematics content. One unit on 2-D geometry at each of the grades 3–5 includes a core of activities that rely on access to computers, either in the classroom or in a lab. Other units on geometry, measurement, data, and changes include computer activities, but can be taught without them. In these units, however, students' experience is greatly enhanced by computer use.

The following list outlines the recommended use of computers in this curriculum. The software is available for download at http://www.scottforesman.com/investigations/software/.

### Kindergarten
Unit: *Making Shapes and Building Blocks*
  (Exploring Geometry)
Software: *MS_Shapes*

### Grade 1
Unit: *Quilt Squares and Block Towns*
  (2-D and 3-D Geometry)
Software: *QS_Shapes*

### Grade 2
Unit: *Mathematical Thinking at Grade 2*
  (Introduction)
Software: *MT_Shapes*

Unit: *Shapes, Halves, and Symmetry*
  (Geometry and Fractions)
Software: *SH_Shapes*

Unit: *How Long? How Far?* (Measuring)
Software: *HL_Geo-Logo*

### Grade 3
Unit: *Flips, Turns, and Area* (2-D Geometry)
Software: *Tumbling Tetrominoes*

Unit: *Turtle Paths* (2-D Geometry)
Software: *TP_Geo-Logo*

### Grade 4
Unit: *Sunken Ships and Grid Patterns*
  (2-D Geometry)
Software: *SS_Geo-Logo*

### Grade 5
Unit: *Picturing Polygons* (2-D Geometry)
Software: *PP_Geo-Logo*

Unit: *Patterns of Change* (Tables and Graphs)
Software: *Trips*

The software for the *Investigations* units uses the power of the computer to help students explore mathematical ideas and relationships that cannot be explored in the same way with physical materials. With the *Shapes* (grades K–2) and *Tumbling Tetrominoes* (grade 3) software, students explore symmetry, pattern, rotation and reflection, area, and characteristics of 2-D shapes. With the *Geo-Logo* software (grades 2–5), students investigate rotation and reflection, coordinate geometry, the properties of 2-D shapes, and angles. The *Trips* software (grade 5) is a mathematical exploration of motion in which students run experiments and interpret data presented in graphs and tables.

We suggest that students work in pairs on the computer; this not only maximizes computer resources but also encourages students to consult, monitor, and teach each other. Generally, more than two students at one computer find it difficult to share. Managing access to computers is an issue for every classroom. The curriculum gives you explicit support for setting up a system. The units are structured on the assumption that you have enough computers for half your students to work on the machines in pairs at one time. If you do not have access to that many computers, suggestions are made for structuring class time to use the unit with fewer than five.

Assessment plays a critical role in teaching and learning, and it is an integral part of the *Investigations* curriculum. For a teacher using these units, assessment is an ongoing process. You observe students' discussions and explanations of their strategies on a daily basis and examine their work as it evolves. While students are busy recording and representing their work, working on projects, sharing with partners, and playing mathematical games, you have many opportunities to observe their mathematical thinking. What you learn through observation guides your decisions about how to proceed. In any of the units, you will repeatedly consider questions like these:

■ Do students come up with their own strategies for solving problems, or do they expect others to tell them what to do? What do their strategies reveal about their mathematical understanding?

■ Do students understand that there are different strategies for solving problems? Do they articulate their strategies and try to understand other students' strategies?

■ How effectively do students use materials as tools to help with their mathematical work?

■ Do students have effective ideas for keeping track of and recording their work? Does keeping track of and recording their work seem difficult for them?

You will need to develop a comfortable and efficient system for recording and keeping track of your observations. Some teachers keep a clipboard handy and jot notes on a class list or on adhesive labels that are later transferred to student files. Others keep loose-leaf notebooks with a page for each student and make weekly notes about what they have observed in class.

## Assessment Tools in the Unit

With the activities in each unit, you will find questions to guide your thinking while observing the students at work. You will also find two built-in assessment tools: Teacher Checkpoints and embedded Assessment activities.

**Teacher Checkpoints** The designated Teacher Checkpoints in each unit offer a time to "check in" with individual students, watch them at work, and ask questions that illuminate how they are thinking.

At first it may be hard to know what to look for, hard to know what kinds of questions to ask. Students may be reluctant to talk; they may not be accustomed to having the teacher ask them about their work, or they may not know how to explain their thinking. Two important ingredients of this process are asking students open-ended questions about their work and showing genuine interest in how they are approaching the task. When students see that you are interested in their thinking and are counting on them to come up with their own ways of solving problems, they may surprise you with the depth of their understanding.

Teacher Checkpoints also give you the chance to pause in the teaching sequence and reflect on how your class is doing overall. Think about whether you need to adjust your pacing: Are most students fluent with strategies for solving a particular kind of problem? Are they just starting to formulate good strategies? Or are they still struggling with how to start? Depending on what you see as the students work, you may want to spend more time on similar problems, change some of the problems to use smaller numbers, move quickly to more challenging material, modify subsequent activities for some students, work on particular ideas with a small group, or pair students who have good strategies with those who are having more difficulty.

**Embedded Assessment Activities** Assessment activities embedded in each unit will help you examine specific pieces of student work, figure out what it means, and provide feedback. From the students' point of view, these assessment activities are no different from any others. Each is a learning experience in and of itself, as well as an opportunity for you to gather evidence about students' mathematical understanding.

The embedded Assessment activities sometimes involve writing and reflecting; at other times, a discussion or brief interaction between student and teacher; and in still other instances, the creation and explanation of a product. In most cases, the assessments require that students *show* what they did, *write* or *talk* about it, or do both. Having to explain how they worked through a problem helps students be more focused and clear in their mathematical thinking. It also helps them realize that doing mathematics is a process that may involve tentative starts, revising one's approach, taking different paths, and working through ideas.

Teachers often find the hardest part of assessment to be interpreting their students' work. We provide guidelines to help with that interpretation. If you have used a process approach to teaching writing, the assessment in *Investigations* will seem familiar. For many of the assessment activities, a Teacher Note provides examples of student work and a commentary on what it indicates about student thinking.

## Documentation of Student Growth

To form an overall picture of mathematical progress, it is important to document each student's work in journals, notebooks, or portfolios. The choice is largely a matter of personal preference; some teachers have students keep a notebook or folder for each unit, while others prefer one mathematics notebook, or a portfolio of selected work for the entire year. The final activity in each *Investigations* unit, called Choosing Student Work to Save, helps you and the students select representative samples for a record of their work.

This kind of regular documentation helps you synthesize information about each student as a mathematical learner. From different pieces of evidence, you can put together the big picture. This synthesis will be invaluable in thinking about where to go next with a particular child, deciding where more work is needed, or explaining to parents (or other teachers) how a child is doing.

If you use portfolios, you need to collect a good balance of work, yet avoid being swamped with an overwhelming amount of paper. Following are some tips for effective portfolios:

■ Collect a representative sample of work, including some pieces that students themselves select for inclusion in the portfolio. There should be just a few pieces for each unit, showing different kinds of work—some assignments that involve writing, as well as some that do not.

■ If students do not date their work, do so yourself so that you can reconstruct the order in which pieces were done.

■ Include your reflections on the work. When you are looking back over the whole year, such comments are reminders of what seemed especially interesting about a particular piece; they can also be helpful to other teachers and to parents. Older students should be encouraged to write their own reflections about their work.

## Assessment Overview

There are two places to turn for a preview of the assessment opportunities in each *Investigations* unit. The Assessment Resources column in the unit Overview Chart (pp. I-13–I-15) identifies the Teacher Checkpoints and Assessment activities embedded in each investigation, guidelines for observing the students that appear within classroom activities, and any Teacher Notes and Dialogue Boxes that explain what to look for and what types of student responses you might expect to see in your classroom. Additionally, the section About the Assessment in This Unit (p. I-18) gives you a detailed list of questions for each investigation, keyed to the mathematical emphases, to help you observe student growth.

**Assessment Sourcebook**  The *Assessment Sourcebook* complements and supports the embedded assessments of *Investigations* by offering further opportunities to gather information about students' growing mathematical understanding.

The *Assessment Sourcebook* provides you with sets of Assessment Tasks and Masters designed to assess your students' understanding of the most important mathematical ideas of the unit. The *Sourcebook* also provides information about the mathematical significance of each assessment task; suggestions on how to observe students and evaluate their work; and unit checklists of mathematical emphases. Each checklist provides space to make short notes about individual students.

The assessments in the *Sourcebook* should be used in addition to other assessments that are presented in each unit. The combination of these assessments, along with samples of student work, will offer a picture of a student's understanding of the mathematical concepts and skills presented in the unit.

# Up and Down the Number Line

**Content of This Unit**  Students investigate ideas about addition and subtraction as they play games and do activities that involve changing the position of a chip on a vertical number line. They use numbers with negative signs from the beginning of the unit. In the third investigation, students play games on boards set up as a horizontal number line. We use small numbers in many of the activities in order to make computations manageable, so students are able to concentrate on the addition and subtraction relationships that are the focus of the unit. Through these investigations, students develop knowledge about numbers below zero, net change, the opposite effects of addition and subtraction, and many ways to use addition and subtraction to reach a given answer.

**Connections with Other Units**  If you are doing the full-year *Investigations* curriculum in the suggested sequence for grade 3, this is the sixth of ten units.

The work in this unit is continued and extended in the grade 3 Addition and Subtraction unit, *Combining and Comparing*, where students score a game by adding positive and negative numbers, and in the grade 4 Graphs unit, *Changes Over Time*, where students make line graphs to show the growth of a plant over time.

This unit can be used successfully at either grade 3 or grade 4, depending on the previous experience and needs of your students.

## *Investigations* Curriculum  ■  Suggested Grade 3 Sequence

*Mathematical Thinking at Grade 3* (Introduction)

*Things That Come in Groups* (Multiplication and Division)

*Flips, Turns, and Area* (2-D Geometry)

*From Paces to Feet* (Measuring and Data)

*Landmarks in the Hundreds* (The Number System)

▶ *Up and Down the Number Line* (Changes)

*Combining and Comparing* (Addition and Subtraction)

*Turtle Paths* (2-D Geometry)

*Fair Shares* (Fractions)

*Exploring Solids and Boxes* (3-D Geometry)

# Investigation 1 ▪ Net Change

| Class Sessions | Activities | Pacing |
|---|---|---|
| Sessions 1 and 2 (p. 4)<br>ELEVATOR TRIPS UP AND DOWN | Planning a Fantasy Skyscraper<br>Finding Net Change<br>Comparing Different Kinds of Trips<br>Using Numbers Off the Chart<br>Homework: Net Change from Start to Finish | minimum<br>2 hr |
| Sessions 3 and 4 (p. 13)<br>MANY WAYS TO MAKE ONE<br>NET CHANGE | Finding Many Ways to Make a Net Change<br>Introducing the Game of Many Changes<br>Playing the Game of Many Changes<br>Teacher Checkpoint: Using Many Changes Cards<br>Homework: Playing the Game of Many Changes at Home | minimum<br>2 hr |
| Session 5 (p. 21)<br>THIRTY CHANGES | Where Does the Elevator End Up?<br>Using Bigger Mixed-Up Changes<br>Homework: Mixed-Up Changes | minimum<br>1 hr |
| Sessions 6 and 7 (p. 23)<br>MISSING INFORMATION PROBLEMS | Missing Starts and Missing Changes<br>Our Own Missing Information Problems<br>More Than One Piece Missing<br>Assessment: Six Changes and a Missing Start | minimum<br>2 hr |
| Session 8 (Excursion)* (p. 29)<br>STOPPING AT MANY FLOORS | Pick Up Chips<br>Homework: Playing Pick Up Chips at Home<br>Extension: Fewest Floors<br>Extension: A Picture of the Game | minimum<br>1 hr |

🕐 Ten-Minute Math ▪ Estimation and Number Sense

* Excursions can be omitted without harming the integrity or continuity of the unit, but offer good mathematical work if you have time to include them.

## Mathematical Emphasis

- Developing the concept of net change

- Developing strategies for computing net change and for using net change to find a missing end point or starting point

- Recognizing that net change is the same regardless of the order in which changes are carried out

- Using a change in the negative direction to cancel a change in the positive direction

- Developing strategies for adding a long sequence of changes, including the use of a calculator

- Constructing different sequences of positive and negative numbers to produce the same net change

## Assessment Resources

More Than One Meaning for −3 (Teacher Note, p. 11)

They're All Different! (Dialogue Box, p. 12)

Teacher Checkpoint: Using Many Changes Cards (p. 18)

Assessment: Six Changes and a Missing Start (p. 26)

Solving Back-in-Time Problems (Teacher Note, p. 26)

Assessment: Six Changes and a Missing Start (Teacher Note, p. 27)

Finding a Missing Start (Dialogue Box, p. 28)

## Materials

Chart paper

Paper and pencils

Stick-on notes, 1½" × 2"

Chips, cubes, or other small objects to use as game pieces

Quart-size resealable plastic bags for holding materials

Scissors

Tape

Paper clips

Crayons, colored pencils, or markers

Overhead projector and transparencies

Calculators

Family letter

Student Sheets 1–9

Teaching resource sheets

# Investigation 2 ▪ Representing Elevator Trips

| Class Sessions | Activities | Pacing |
|---|---|---|
| Session 1 (p. 34)<br>GRAPHING ELEVATOR TRIPS | Inventing Ways to Represent Trips<br>Discussing the Graphs<br>Homework: Change-Over-Time Graphs | minimum<br>1 hr |
| Sessions 2 and 3 (p. 37)<br>REPEATING ELEVATOR TRIPS | Graphs That Show Change Over Time<br>Teacher Checkpoint: Graphing a Set of Changes<br>Graphing Repeating Trips<br>Analyzing the Graphs<br>Extension: Up and Up, Down and Down | minimum<br>2 hr |
| Session 4 (p. 42)<br>PLUS AND MINUS GRAPHS | Introducing Plus and Minus Graphs<br>Making Plus and Minus Graphs<br>Matching Graphs<br>Assessment: Repeating Elevator Problem<br>Homework: Net Change on a Graph | minimum<br>1 hr |

◑ **Ten-Minute Math** ▪ **Estimation and Number Sense**

## Mathematical Emphasis

- Representing numbers graphically

- Interpreting changes in direction on a graph

- Understanding how the passage of time is represented on graphs showing change over time

- Finding net change on graphs

- Comparing overall shapes of graphs

## Assessment Resources

Students' Graphs of Elevator Trips (Teacher Note, p. 36)

Teacher Checkpoint: Graphing a Set of Changes (p. 38)

Assessment: Repeating Elevator Problem (p. 44)

## Materials

Plain paper

Crayons, colored pencils, or markers

Tape

Overhead projector and transparencies

Student Sheets 10–13

Teaching resource sheets

# Investigation 3 ▪ Inventing Board Games

| Class Sessions | Activities | Pacing |
|---|---|---|
| Session 1 (p. 48)<br>PLAYING A BOARD GAME | Save the Siberian Tiger<br>Homework: Playing Save the Siberian Tiger at Home | minimum<br>1 hr |
| Sessions 2 and 3 (p. 52)<br>CREATING A BOARD GAME | Designing a Board Game<br>Trying Out the Games<br>Choosing Student Work to Save<br>Homework: Finishing at Home<br>Extension: Sharing the Games<br>Extension: Setting Up a Games Center | minimum<br>2 hr |

## Mathematical Emphasis

- Relating the direction of movement (left or right, up or down) to positive and negative numbers

- Using net change to determine an end point

## Assessment Resources

Choosing Student Work to Save (p. 53)

## Materials

Scissors

Tape

Chips or other game pieces

Snap™ Cubes or other counters

Crayons, colored pencils, or markers

Calculators

Student Sheet 14

Teaching resource sheets

Following are the basic materials needed for the activities in this unit.

- Cubes, or other objects to use as game pieces, 10 per student

- Snap Cubes™ (interlocking cubes) or other counters: 50 per student (optional)

- Chart paper

- Resealable plastic bags, quart size: 1 per student

- Calculators: at least 1 per pair of students

- Stick-on notes, small: 2 pads

- Scissors, 1 per student

- Paper clips

- Colored pencils, crayons, or markers

- Glue or paste, tape

- Plain paper

- Overhead projector

The following materials are provided at the end of this unit as blackline masters. A Student Activity Booklet containing all student sheets and teaching resources needed for individual work is available.

Family Letter (p. 60)

Student Sheets 1–14 (p. 61)

Teaching Resources:

Skyscraper (p. 70)

Net Change Cards (p. 71)

One-Centimeter Graph Paper (p. 76)

Graphs Showing Change Over Time (p. 77)

Repeating Elevator Graphs (p. 78)

Small Plus and Minus Cards (p. 79)

Large Plus and Minus Cards (p. 80)

Tiger Gameboard (p. 83)

Tiger Cards (p. 85)

Make-Your-Own Gameboard (p. 87)

Changes Cards (p. 89)

Practice Pages (p. 91)

## Related Children's Literature

Dahl, Roald. *Charlie and the Great Glass Elevator.* New York: Puffin Books, 1972.

Froman, Robert. *Less Than Nothing Is Really Something.* New York: Thomas Y. Crowell, 1973.

In solving arithmetic problems, it is useful to distinguish two areas of knowledge: (1) counting and computing, and (2) relations between numbers and operations. Examples of the first area include knowing how to count, knowing procedures for adding and subtracting, and knowing *when* to add or subtract. Examples of the second are knowing that addition increases the result, knowing that subtraction cancels addition, and knowing that the order of successive additions and subtractions does not affect the result.

The two areas are critical and interrelated. Knowledge of number relations allows us to assess whether the result of a computation makes sense. For instance, if we get a result of 15 + 19 that is less than the 15 or 19, we recognize that something is wrong. This recognition is based on what we know about how addition works.

Many of the mathematical ideas in this unit focus on number relations in addition and subtraction. So that the relations can be made clear, we add and subtract only small numbers. "Changes" is what we call the moves up and down the number line as we add or subtract. Some central ideas about the relationships among these changes are as follows:

- Combinations of changes have a total effect or net change that does not depend on the starting position or on the order of the changes. For example, from any starting point, the changes −3 +1 −1 (or, in a different order, −1 −3 +1) make a net change of negative 3.

- It is possible to get from any number to any number in any number of changes. The same net (total) change can be achieved with any number of changes. For example, +2 can be made with +1 +1, +3 −2 +1, +3 +1 −3 +1, or an infinite variety of other combinations of changes.

- Positive net changes can be made with some negative changes, and negative net changes can be made with some positive changes. For example, a net change of +2 can be made with +1 +1 and with +3 −1. In strings of changes, pairs of opposites such as +2 and −2 have a net change

of zero and so can be eliminated from the calculations. Long strings of changes can be made using opposites: +2 +1 −1 +3 −3 +2 −2 still make a net change of +2.

**Mathematical Emphasis**   At the beginning of each investigation, the Mathematical Emphasis section tells you what is most important for students to learn about during that investigation. Many of these understandings and processes are difficult and complex. Students gradually learn more and more about each idea over many years of schooling. Individual students will begin and end the unit with different levels of knowledge and skill, but all will gain greater knowledge of number relations in addition and subtraction.

Throughout the *Investigations* curriculum, there are many opportunities for ongoing daily assessment as you observe, listen to, and interact with students at work. In this unit, you will find two Teacher Checkpoints:

Investigation 1, Sessions 3–4:
Using Many Changes Cards (p. 18)

Investigation 2, Sessions 2–3:
Graphing a Set of Changes (p. 38)

This unit also has two embedded Assessment activities:

Investigation 1, Sessions 6–7:
Six Changes and a Missing Start (p. 26)

Investigation 2, Session 4:
Repeating Elevator Problem (p. 44)

In addition, you can use almost any activity in this unit to assess your students' needs and strengths. Listed below are questions to help you focus your observation in each investigation. You may want to keep track of your observations for each student to help you plan your curriculum and monitor students' growth. Suggestions for documenting student growth can be found in the section About Assessment (p. I–10).

## Investigation 1: Net Change

- Do students understand how net change is calculated? How do they talk about net change in relation to starting and ending points of a sequence of changes?

- Do students use net change in appropriate ways? For example, can they use net change to find the missing starting point of a sequence of changes?

- Do students recognize that a series of changes produces the same net change, regardless of the order of the changes? Do they understand why this is the case?

- Do students know how to combine negative and positive changes?

- How do students add long sequences of numbers? Can they use the calculator effectively? How do they keep track of where they are in the calculation? What different strategies and recording procedures do they use when they are not using the calculator?

- Given a net change, can students construct several different sequences that have that net change? How do they do it? Do they modify an earlier sequence or start from scratch each time?

## Investigation 2: Representing Elevator Trips

- How are students communicating about change over time through their representations? Are they able to clearly represent numbers graphically?

- Do students understand that a "going up" graph indicates positive change, a "going down" graph indicates negative change, and a horizontal graph indicates zero change?

- Do students recognize that the passage of time (or order of events) can be represented by moving from left to right?

- What strategies do students use to find net change on graphs?

- How do students describe the overall shapes of graphs? Do they use the overall shapes to compare graphs?

## Investigation 3: Inventing Board Games

- How do students understand and explain the difference between moving up and down or left and right on a graph showing change over time? Do they know that positive and negative changes are in opposite directions?

- Are students able to use net change to determine an end point rather than counting out each change separately?

### Assessment Sourcebook

In the *Assessment Sourcebook* you will find End-of-Unit Assessment Tasks and Assessment Masters available in English and Spanish. You will also find suggestions to help you observe and evaluate student work and checklists of mathematical emphases with space for you to record individual student information.

In the *Investigations* curriculum, mathematical vocabulary is introduced naturally during the activities. We don't ask students to learn definitions of new terms; rather, they come to understand such words as *factor* or *area* or *symmetry* by hearing them used frequently in discussion as they investigate new concepts. This approach is compatible with current theories of second-language acquisition, which emphasize the use of new vocabulary in meaningful contexts while students are actively involved with objects, pictures, and physical movement.

Listed below are some key words used in this unit that will not be new to most English speakers at this age level but may be unfamiliar to students with limited English proficiency. You will want to spend additional time working on these words with your students who are learning English. If your students are working with a second-language teacher, you might enlist your colleague's aid in familiarizing students with these words, before and during this unit. In the classroom, look for opportunities for students to hear and use these words. Activities you can use to present the words are given in the appendix, Vocabulary Support for Second-Language Learners (p. 57).

**skyscraper, floor, ground level, elevator, button**
A diagram of a *skyscraper* with many *floors,* some above and some below *ground level,* is the model for introducing the number line in this unit. Students go up and down by way of an imaginary *elevator* with both positive and negative numbers on its *buttons*.

**starting, ending**   As students move either up and down or back and forth along the number line through a specified set of changes, they identify their *starting* and *ending* positions by number.

**gain, lose**   Students play games in which they *gain* and *lose* chips, according to the directions on the space, as they move along a number-line gameboard.

**opposite**   A number with a minus sign (a negative number) is presented as the *opposite* of the same number with a plus sign (a positive number). For example, a net change of –3 is the opposite of a net change of +3.

In addition to these key words, students will encounter terms related to endangered wildlife as they come up in the Save the Siberian Tiger game: *tiger, cubs, habitat, fox, wolf, boars, deer, destroy, hunting.* Familiarity with these words will be helpful but not critical as students play the board game in Investigation 3.

### Multicultural Extensions for All Students
Whenever possible, encourage students to share words, objects, customs, or any aspects of daily life from their own cultures and backgrounds that are relevant to the activities in this unit. For example:

- In Investigation 3, when students create games, some might bring in games from their culture to teach to their classmates. Students who have lived in other countries might base their game-boards on places familiar to them; this can be a good basis for class discussion of geographical and cultural differences and similarities.

# Investigations

# INVESTIGATION 1

# Net Change

## What Happens

**Sessions 1 and 2: Elevator Trips Up and Down**
Students plan the layout of a fantasy skyscraper
for children and prepare their own skyscraper
diagrams and changes cards. They choose a
starting floor and an ending floor and figure out
the net change (how far and in what direction
they have moved).

**Sessions 3 and 4: Many Ways to Make One Net
Change** Students find many sets of changes that
make the same net change. They play a game in
which they use as many changes as they can to
make a given net change.

**Session 5: Thirty Changes** Students post a
sequence of 30 changes along a wall. Working in
groups, they find out what the total or net effect
of applying all the changes would be. They use
strategies they have learned, such as –2 cancels
+2, so if they count three –2's and five +2's, they
know they need to consider only the extra two
+2's.

**Sessions 6 and 7: Missing Information
Problems** Students solve changes problems in
which critical information is missing: either the
starting point or one or more of the changes.
They write about their strategies for finding a
missing starting floor.

**Session 8 (Excursion): Stopping at Many
Floors** Students play a game in which they
arrange a set of changes to make the elevator
stop on as many different floors as they can.

## Mathematical Emphasis

- Developing the concept of net change, which
  specifies both how far and in which direction
  (positive or negative) an object has moved in all
  after a series of moves in each direction

- Developing strategies for computing net change
  and for using net change to find a missing end
  point or starting point

- Recognizing that net change is the same
  regardless of the order in which changes are
  carried out

- Using a change in the negative direction to
  cancel a change in the positive direction

- Developing strategies for adding a long
  sequence of changes, including the use of a
  calculator

- Constructing different sequences of positive
  and negative numbers to produce the same net
  change

## What to Plan Ahead of Time

### Materials

- Chart paper (Sessions 1–4)
- Stick-on notes, 1½" × 2" or a bit larger: 2 pads (Sessions 1–7)
- Chips, cubes, or other small objects to use as game pieces: 10 per student (Sessions 1–4, 6–8)
- Quart-size resealable plastic bags for holding materials: 1 per student (Sessions 1–4, 6–8)
- Scissors: 1 per student (Sessions 1–4)
- Tape for assembling skyscrapers (Sessions 1–2)
- Paper clips: 1 per student (Sessions 3–4)
- Crayons, colored pencils, or markers (Sessions 3–4)
- Paper and pencils (Session 8)
- Calculators: 1 per student (Sessions 3–5)
- Overhead projector (Sessions 1–4)

### Other Preparation

- Duplicate student sheets and teaching resources (located at the end of this unit) in the following quantities. If you have Student Activity Booklets, copy only the items marked with an asterisk, including any transparencies and extra materials needed.

*For Sessions 1–2*

Student Sheet 1, Net Change from Start to Finish (p. 61): 2 per student (1 for homework)

Skyscraper (p. 70): 2 per student (1 for homework), and 1 transparency*

Family letter* (p. 60): 1 per student. Remember to sign it before copying.

*For Sessions 3–4*

Student Sheet 2, Net Change with Many Changes (p. 62): 2 per student (1 for homework)

Changes Cards (p. 89): 2 sets per student (1 for homework)

Net Change Cards (p. 71): 1 set per student

Student Sheet 3, How to Play the Game of Many Changes (p. 63): 1 per student

Student Sheet 4, Many Changes to Make +2 (p. 64): 1 per student

*For Session 5*

Student Sheet 5, Mixed-Up Changes (p. 65): 1 per student (homework)

*For Sessions 6–7*

Student Sheet 6, Missing Information Problems (p. 66): 1 per student, plus some extras*

Student Sheet 7, Six Changes and a Missing Start (p. 67): 1 per student

*For Session 8*

Student Sheet 8, Pick Up Chips (p. 68): 1 per pair or group (class), 1 per student (homework), and 1 transparency*

Student Sheet 9, How to Play Pick Up Chips (p. 69): 1 per student (homework)

- Assemble one skyscraper as an example. Or, to save time, assemble skyscrapers for all students. (Session 1, optional)
- Cut small stick-on note pads in half, with sticky backing on each piece, making a mini-pad of 8–10 notes for each student.
- Try all the games yourself or with a few students before you play them with the whole class. (Sessions 3–4, 8)
- If you plan to provide folders in which students will save their work for the entire unit, prepare these for distribution during Session 1.

# Elevator Trips Up and Down

### What Happens

Students plan the layout of a fantasy skyscraper for children and prepare their own skyscraper diagrams and changes cards. They choose a starting floor and an ending floor and figure out the net change (how far and in what direction they have moved). Student work focuses on:

- finding net change given a starting and an ending number
- recognizing direction of change
- finding trips with the same net change

## Materials

- Skyscraper transparency
- Chart paper
- Stick-on notes
- Game pieces (1 per student)
- Resealable plastic bags (1 per student)
- Scissors (1 per student)
- Tape
- Student Sheet 1 (2 per student, 1 to be used for homework)
- Skyscraper sheet or assembled skyscrapers (2 per student, 1 to be used for homework)
- Family letter
- Overhead projector

## Planning a Fantasy Skyscraper

Display the transparency of the skyscraper. (Alternatively, prepare a similar diagram on chart paper or on the board. Leave some numbers blank at both ends and label middle spaces with numbers 4, 3, 2, 1, 0, 1, 2, 3.) Introduce the skyscraper to the class:

**Who has been inside a tall building? What's the highest floor you have been to? the lowest? How many floors below ground level have you been?**

**What buildings do you know of with elevators? What buildings do you know of with many floors below ground level?**

We are going to plan some make-believe trips in an elevator that goes up and down in a very unusual building that has no top floor and no bottom floor. It is a skyscraper that has more floors than you can count both above the ground and under the ground. The elevator can go up and up forever, and it can go down and down forever. This unusual building is a skyscraper made especially for children.

Floor 0 is the entrance, or ground floor. It is this way that floors are numbered in most other countries. The first floor is one up from the street.

Ask students to close their eyes and imagine what could be on some of the floors of this building—a swimming pool, trampoline, pizza parlor, library, basketball court, and so on. Label some floors above and below ground level according to the students' ideas.

To maintain the sense of a building, write on the lines (rather than the center of the spaces) to label the floors. You need not label all the floors now. Students can fill in others and extend the range of labeled floors on their own skyscrapers.

**Labeling Floors Below Ground** Hold a brief discussion about how to number the floors *below zero* to distinguish them from the floors above. Although minus signs are one possibility, we use minus numbers in these activities to show the downward change in an elevator trip. To make clear the difference between floor numbers and changes, you and your students might choose not to use the minus sign to label the floors below zero.

Some classes have labeled the floors 1B, 2B, 3B, and so on for "below ground" or "basement." If you do decide to label the floors in the same way as the changes (–3, –2, –1, 0 . . . ), speak of the floors as being "below zero," instead of as minus (e.g., 2 below 0), to make clear that these are positions rather than changes. See the **Teacher Note**, More Than One Meaning for –3 (p. 11), for more discussion of this potential confusion.

On your skyscraper transparency or large diagram, mark the numbers below zero in the way the class decides.

**Preparing the Skyscrapers** Hand out the Skyscraper sheet. Students cut along the dotted lines, then tape the two pieces together, with zero in the middle, to make a skyscraper (skipping this step if you have preassembled them). They put their names on the backs of their skyscrapers. They continue the numbering to higher and lower floors, marking the floor numbers below zero in the way the class has decided.

· · · · · · · · · · · · · · · · · · · · · · · · · · · · · · · · · · · · · · · · ·

❖ **Tip for the Linguistically Diverse Classroom** Students draw pictures to show what is on the various floors of the skyscraper, using rebuses instead of words to label the floors. They draw in their ideas for any blank floors.

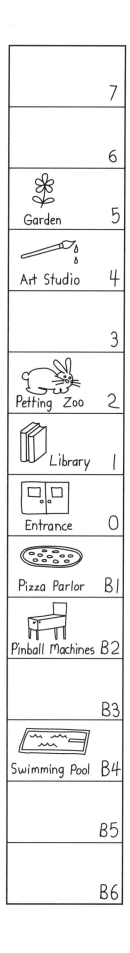

# Finding Net Change

**Introducing Net Change**   Hand out mini-pads of small stick-on notes to each student. Students write Start on one note and End or Finish on another. (Make your own Start and End notes to use with your demonstration skyscraper.) Hand out a chip or game piece to each student. (You may want to hand out resealable bags for storage of the stick-on notes and chips, and the Changes Cards that students will get in the next session.)

Write this chart on the board, leaving room for more entries:

| Starting Floor | Ending Floor | Net Change |
|---|---|---|
| 2 | 5 | |

Mark these starting and ending floors with your labels on the demonstration skyscraper. Students put their Start and End labels in the same places on their skyscrapers.

**How many floors do I travel to make this trip? Try it out on your own skyscraper.**

After students have a chance to figure it out, count while moving your stick-on note up the skyscraper:

**Start at 2, move to 3, 4, 5. How many floors is that?**

Once the class has agreed on the total change, write the number of floors moved, 3, on your chart under Net Change.

**Did I Move Up or Down?**   Ask students in what direction you moved. Write a plus sign (+) in front of the 3 in the net change column, explaining that it stands for a move *up*. Tell students that net change shows both how many floors and *in what direction* they moved.

Choose new starting and ending floors, this time for a trip that moves down. Students put their Start and End labels on the floors you have chosen and figure out the net change.

| Starting Floor | Ending Floor | Net Change |
|---|---|---|
| 2 | 5 | +3 |
| 3 | B2 | −5 |

Ask two student volunteers to come up to your demonstration skyscraper (either transparency or large diagram) to act out a third example.

**Choose a floor to start on. Then choose a floor you want to go to. Put the Start label on the starting floor and the End label on the floor you are going to.**

Add the starting and ending floors that students choose to the chart. For example:

| Starting Floor | Ending Floor | Net Change |
|:---:|:---:|:---:|
| 2 | 5 | +3 |
| 3 | B2 | −5 |
| B1 | 2 | |

**How many floors do you need to go on your trip from your start to your finish? Do you need to go up or down?**

The two students count out the floors, note the direction, and say what they think the net change is. When everyone agrees, record the net change on the chart.

You might repeat this procedure with other volunteers, perhaps some students who are less sure and who want to see if they understand.

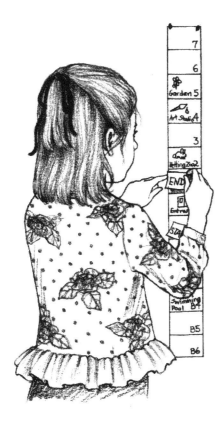

**Finding Net Change from Start to Finish**  Hand out Student Sheet 1, Net Change from Start to Finish. Students use this sheet to record their moves on their skyscrapers. They work in pairs or small groups for 5 to 10 minutes as follows:

One student chooses a starting floor. Another chooses an ending floor. Each student in the group marks these on his or her own skyscraper with Start and End labels. Students figure out the net change and then compare their results. For each problem they do, they fill in the Starting Floor, Ending Floor, and Net Change columns on their charts (Student Sheet 1). If students feel that their skyscrapers aren't tall enough, they can imagine more floors along the desk or table, or even add another paper strip of floors.

While students are working, observe to see that they are figuring net change accurately. Ask them to show you their methods. Some students will mistakenly count out changes beginning with the starting floor instead of the next space above or below. It is important that all students agree to the convention of counting one change for each new floor. If you start at 4 and go to 7, you move your counter to floors 5, 6, and 7 in 3 moves.

Collect two or three trips that students are finding somewhat difficult. Look for problems on which they disagree so that they will be motivated to check their moves. Write the Start and End numbers of these trips on the class chart.

**Checking Net Change**  As a whole class, students consider the new problems on the class chart. Take a poll to find their ideas about the net changes for those problems. Write all answers that the students suggest.

**How might we check the answers on the chart?**

One way to check is to add the net change number to the starting floor number. You should get the ending floor number. Many students will just start at the starting floor on their skyscrapers and count out the net change to see if they finish at the ending floor. Encourage students to try both ways: using their skyscrapers and computing with numbers.

Students work independently for a short time to check the answers on the class chart and also on their own charts. Then bring the students together to report on what they learned. Help the class reach agreement on the correct answers for the problems on the class chart. If there is any disagreement, encourage them to defend their solutions and keep looking for agreement.

## Comparing Different Kinds of Trips

You might begin Session 2 with an investigation of trips that have beginning and ending numbers that appear similar but have different net changes. Pose a set of problems, like those shown in the example below, with similar starting and ending numbers. Write the starting and ending floors, and leave the net changes for the students to figure out. Label each trip in some way (letters or numbers) for purposes of discussion.

In this example, every trip starts on the second floor above or below ground and ends on the fifth floor above or below ground, but each net change is different.

|     | Starting Floor | Ending Floor | Net Change | Answers |
| --- | --- | --- | --- | --- |
| A.  | B2 | 5  |    | +7 |
| B.  | B2 | B5 |    | −3 |
| C.  | 2  | B5 |    | −7 |
| D.  | 2  | 5  |    |    |

Working with partners, students figure out the net change for each trip and record it on their net change chart (Student Sheet 1).

If students seem to be comfortable finding these net changes, make four new problems by reversing the starting and ending floors of your first set. Leave the other four on display so that students can compare them.

|     | Starting Floor | Ending Floor | Net Change | Answers |
| --- | --- | --- | --- | --- |
| E.  | 5  | B2 |    | −7 |
| F.  | B5 | B2 |    | +3 |
| G.  | B5 | 2  |    | +7 |
| H.  | 5  | 2  |    |    |

When students have had a chance to figure these out, hold a group discussion for students to give the answers and explain their methods. See the **Dialogue Box**, They're All Different! (p. 12), for a typical discussion.

**Finding Trips with the Same Net Change**   When the net change column is filled in and the students are in agreement about the answers, ask students to look for patterns in the problems A–H.

**What patterns do you see? Why do you think some of the trips have the same net change? For example, why are trips A and G both +7?**

After discussing some pairs of problems that have the same net change, challenge students to find several other starting and ending combinations that have the same net change. Pick one of the net changes you have just been discussing. For example:

**Find some more pairs of starting and ending floors that have a net change of +7. Use some starting numbers below zero.**

## Using Numbers Off the Chart

Throughout this unit, we make suggestions that students try the same activities with larger numbers. Here is a way to extend the net change activity students have been doing in these sessions.

**Try some examples with a starting or ending number that is not on your skyscraper diagram. For example, when you start at 100 above and go to 2 below, what is the net change?**

Write this problem on the board and have students copy it on their charts. Students work in pairs to figure it out. Don't take answers until everyone has had a chance to work on the problem. Instead, challenge quick finishers with another problem, for example:

**Start at 50 above. Go to 125 above. What is the net change?**

Some students will enjoy doing these problems. Others will not be ready to extend these ideas beyond what they can count out. However, be sure that all students can count net change correctly on their skyscrapers and can check their answers in some way.

## Sessions 1 and 2 Follow-Up

 **Homework**

**Net Change from Start to Finish** Students take home the family letter or the *Investigations* at Home booklet, a second Skyscraper to make for home use, and their Student Sheet 1 from these sessions. For homework, they find net change for more starting and ending floors and add these trips to their charts. Challenge students who are ready to use starting and ending numbers that are not on their skyscrapers.

# More Than One Meaning for −3

One use for negative numbers is to show location on the number line. Vertical number lines are marked with positive numbers above zero, and negative numbers (indicated by a minus sign) below zero. Positive locations are usually written without a plus sign.

Horizontal number lines are marked with positive numbers located to the right of zero and negative numbers located to the left of zero.

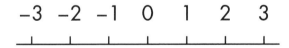

We also use plus and minus signs to indicate changes in position along the number line. A change in position upward or to the right is positive (indicated by a plus sign); a change that runs downward or to the left is negative (indicated by a minus sign).

In this unit, plus and minus signs are used in both ways: to indicate a location on the number line, and to describe a displacement or change along the number line.

We have found that students naturally use a minus sign to denote change. However, they are less apt to use it to describe location, and tend to describe the positions below zero in other ways, including "before zero," "below zero." Sometimes, if they have heard it before, they will refer to such a position as "minus ___."

Feel free to use their words and your own interchangeably. Using a written symbol other than a minus sign is also fine to denote a negative position; it helps avoid confusion between the two meanings.

A third use of the minus sign is for a reversal of operation, so that −(−3) means the opposite of minus three, or plus three. Many calculators have an inverse key (+/−) that performs this operation. Some students may use this operation of reversing signs in the missing information problems in Sessions 6 and 7, to find the starting floor when they know the changes and the ending floor.

## They're All Different!

Students are discussing the difference in net change in trips that look similar, as described in the activity on p. 9.

|  | Starting Floor | Ending Floor | Net Change |
|---|---|---|---|
| **A.** | B2 | 5 |  |
| **B.** | B2 | B5 |  |
| **C.** | 2 | B5 |  |
| **D.** | 2 | 5 |  |

**Michael:** The first one, that's up 7. You go 2 up and then 5 more.

**Does everyone agree?** [*Writes +7 under Net Change.*]

**Tamara:** I get minus 7 for trip B. Two below and 5 below is minus 7.

**Elena:** No, they're closer to each other, both underground.

**What do you think the net change is?**

**Elena:** OK, 2 below down to 3 below. That's 1. And 3 below down to 4 below. That's 2. Then 4 below down to 5 below. That's 3 … minus.

**So that's minus three.** [*Writes in –3 on the chart.*]

**Tyrell:** The next one [trip C] is backwards of the first one. Instead of going up from 2 under to 5 above, you go down from the 2 to the 5.

**Laurie Jo:** Yes. It's minus 7.

[*Writes –7 on the chart.*] **And the last one? Saloni, why don't you tell us about that one?**

**Saloni:** Oh, that's easy. You just go up 3.

**What should I write?**

**Saloni:** Plus 3.

**Let's try some more. Some of you quieter folks, let's hear your opinions about these.** [*Adds four more to the chart, reversing the starting and ending floors from the first four problems.*]

|  | Starting Floor | Ending Floor | Net Change |
|---|---|---|---|
| **E.** | 5 | B2 |  |
| **F.** | B5 | B2 |  |
| **G.** | B5 | 2 |  |
| **H.** | 5 | 2 |  |

**Ryan:** But they're all the same. You can just copy the same answers.

**So, what do you think is the answer to problem E?**

**Ryan:** It's plus 7 like the first one on top, and then its minus 3, minus 7, plus 3.

**Hm. Should I write in Ryan's answers?**

**Ly Dinh:** I think the first one is upside down of A. You go down instead of up, so it's minus 7.

**How can we check this one?**

**Saloni:** Start at 5 and go down 7. You go down 5 to the 0 floor and then 2 more to B2. I think Ly Dinh is right.

The discussion continues until the class agrees on the answers to E through H.

**Ryan** [*who hasn't spoken since Ly Dinh disagreed with his answer*]: They're all different!

Although we encourage students to look for patterns, it is important that they keep checking to see if the patterns work on the model they are using. Ryan sees similarities between the numbers in the two sets of problems, but when Ly Dinh checks the direction of travel, he finds out that they are opposites.

# Many Ways to Make One Net Change

## What Happens

Students find many sets of changes that make the same net change. They play a game in which they use as many changes as they can to make a given net change. Students' work focuses on:

- making the same net change in many different ways using positive and negative numbers
- recognizing that the net change is the same regardless of the order of changes
- adding a series of integers
- using subtraction to cancel addition

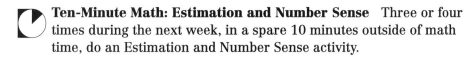 **Ten-Minute Math: Estimation and Number Sense**   Three or four times during the next week, in a spare 10 minutes outside of math time, do an Estimation and Number Sense activity.

For about a minute, show students a problem involving several additions and subtractions. Ask them to do the problem mentally to get as near as they can to the answer. Use examples in which reordering the numbers will make the problem easier to solve. Adjust the difficulty and the exposure time for your students. Do two or three problems in a ten-minute session. Some possibilities:

$10 - 7 + 6 + 27 =$

$29 + 3 + 2 - 28 =$

$200 + 50 - 25 + 50 - 25 =$

After a minute or less, cover the problem and take a poll of all answers. Uncover the problem and allow more time for students to compute mentally. Then have students share how they figured it out. For full directions and variations, see pp. 55–56.

## Materials

- All materials from Sessions 1 and 2 except Student Sheet 1
- Students' assembled skyscrapers
- Paper clips (1 per student)
- Student Sheet 2 (2 per student, 1 to be used for homework)
- Student Sheet 3 (1 per student)
- Student Sheet 4 (1 per student)
- Changes Cards (2 sets per student, 1 to be used for homework)
- Net Change Cards (1 set per student)
- Scissors (1 per student)
- Crayons, colored pencils, or markers
- Calculators

## Finding Many Ways to Make a Net Change

**Preparing Changes Cards**   Hand out one sheet of Changes Cards to each student. Before cutting them apart, students should use crayons to mark the entire back of their sheets in a distinctive pattern (stripes, zigzags, blotches, a pattern of their initials) so they can recognize their own cards once they are cut out. Before starting, ask students to look at the page.

**What different numbers are on the cards? How many of each number are there? How many number cards will you have when you cut them out?**

As the students cut out their cards, give everyone a paper clip to keep the cards together. They will need to keep their full set of 20 to use throughout this unit.

**Introducing Elevator Change Buttons**   Remind students about the buttons in real elevators.

**How do you tell an elevator what floor you want to go to?** (When you get in the elevator, you or the elevator operator pushes the button for that floor.)

**The buttons in our make-believe skyscraper are different. They are "change" buttons. Instead of pushing the number of the floor where you want to go, you push the amount you want to go up or down. The buttons on your elevator are the same as the Changes Cards you cut out.**

**If I were on the second floor and I pushed –3, where would I end up?** (Count this out on the diagram to show the students.)

**To go from the third floor to the fifth floor, what button should I push?**

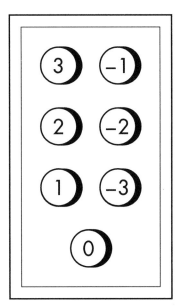

❖   **Tip for the Linguistically Diverse Classroom**   Point to the floors as you ask the questions. You might draw a panel of "elevator buttons" labeled with appropriate changes to help dramatize the questions.

Determining what button to push is the same as what the students did in Sessions 1 and 2—figuring net change, given the start and end. Write a few more problems on the board for students to try. For example:

**What button would we push to go from floor 3 to floor B2? To go from B3 to 3?**

**If we start at 4 and push +3, where do we end up? If we start at 2 and push –3, where do we end up?**

**Using Several Changes**   Introduce the idea of making several changes to get to your destination.

**Now you are going to plan trips on the elevator by using more than one change. Suppose you like to ride around in the elevator and stop at several floors before getting to your destination.**

Put your Start label at any floor other than zero. (If you start at zero, students may conclude that where you end up is always the same as the net change.) Pick three Changes Cards (or ask students to pick them). Read them one by one, and move your piece accordingly, asking students to direct you. Put your End label at the floor where you end up. Ask students what the net change is.

Write the net change on the board and challenge students to suggest ways to make the same net change using three different changes, then four changes, then five changes. Collect a few examples and write them on the board.

Distribute Student Sheet 2, Net Change with Many Changes, one per student. Working in pairs or small groups, students use their Changes Cards to make more sets of changes for the same net change. They lay out the Changes Cards in front of them and can try out the changes on their skyscrapers if they wish. They record their sets of changes on Student Sheet 2. Suggest that students write some of the different sets they found on the board.

Let your students decide (as the issues come up) how many zeros are allowed, whether you can use changes larger than –3 and +3, and whether a different order of the same changes counts as a different set.

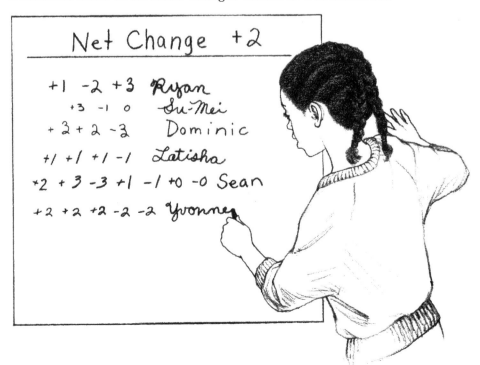

**Negative and Zero Net Change**   Choose some other net changes, perhaps a small negative net change and a net change of zero, and ask students to find combinations of changes for them. See the **Dialogue Box**, Making a Net Change of −4 (p. 20).

To get students thinking about zero net change, ask them how they might ride around in the elevator and end up back where they started. Encourage students to find a long series of changes that has a certain net change.

**Checking with a Calculator**   While students are working, suggest they get out calculators to check the net change sets on the board and also on their own lists. Students can help each other do this. They press each symbol in turn (sign, number, sign, number, etc.) until they get to the end of the list. Then they press the equal sign to get the net change.

---

## Activity

## Introducing the Game of Many Changes

The purpose of this game is to use as many changes as possible to make a certain net change. Introduce the game to the whole group, using your skyscraper transparency or diagram. Put your Start label on any number except zero. Choose a Net Change Card and write the number on the board. Ask students where you will end up with that net change. Put your End label there.

Deal yourself seven Changes Cards and write the seven changes on the board. The students pick the same seven changes from their decks and lay them out in front of them.

**How can we use two of our Changes Cards to make this net change? Is there a way we can use more than two cards to make the same net change? Can we use five or six cards?**

Collect a few ideas from students.

Explain that students are now going to play a sample round of the Game of Many Changes. Let someone choose another starting point (other than zero). Students all deal themselves seven Changes Cards. Pick a Net Change Card or have a student pick one, at random. Write this net change on the board. Students use as many of their seven Changes Cards as they can to achieve that net change.

Observe groups to be sure students have the idea of using more than one or two cards. Encourage students to help each other. Students can check their own and each other's solutions by counting on the skyscraper, by computing mentally, or by using a calculator.

Players use Student Sheet 2, Net Change with Many Changes, to record both the net change and the changes they used to achieve it.

This might be a good stopping point for Session 3; you can begin Session 4 with students playing the game. To save time during math class, you might hand out the Net Change Cards (p. 71) for students to cut apart before Session 4.

## Playing the Game of Many Changes

Be sure each group has one set of Net Change Cards. Then distribute Student Sheet 3, How to Play the Game of Many Changes, and review the game rules with students. (Students should save these sheets to take home with the other materials for homework after Session 4.) Each student should have a game piece.

Students play the game one on one, or one pair against another. Each player or pair takes seven Changes Cards. Players place these face up in front of them. The set of Net Change Cards goes face down in the middle of the group. One player turns over the top Net Change Card.

All players use as many of their seven Changes Cards as possible to make the net change shown on the Net Change Card. Players check each other's sets of changes to see if they work. They write the changes they used and the net changes on Student Sheet 2.

For the next round, each player starts with seven new Changes Cards. Someone turns up a new Net Change Card.

**Note:** Some students may find it helpful to use stick-on notes to mark a start and end on their skyscrapers for a trip that fits the net change, and then count out the changes to check. Others may do the problems without using their skyscraper at all; they might construct equations of each set of changes with the net change as the answer. When you observe students playing, encourage those who always use the skyscraper to check their sets of changes by adding and subtracting mentally or with a calculator.

**Teaching the Variation** A group of students who were frustrated by the sets of changes they were getting when they picked seven cards at random invented this variation: Players pick five Changes Cards at random and use as many as they can to make the net change. Then they turn the remainder of the Changes Cards deck face up and deliberately choose two more. The goal is to use all seven cards.

If you decide to use the variation, you can teach it to small groups of students or to the whole class at once. An example of a turn for one player might be as follows: The net change is +1, and the first five cards are 0, –2, + 2, +2, –3. The player uses four of the cards, 0, +2, +2, –3, to make a net of +1, but cannot use the –2. What two cards should the player pick so as to use all seven of the cards? The two cards must add +2 to cancel out the extra –2, so any of these pairs would good choices: +1 and +1, +3 and –1, or +2 and 0.

**Discussing Strategies** After several rounds, bring the class together briefly to share strategies. Students can give examples of instances when they used lots of cards. These strategies will be useful in the next activity.

<hr>

## Activity

### Teacher Checkpoint

### Using Many Changes Cards

In this checkpoint activity, you can get a good idea of your students' understanding of net change and a sense of who has begun to develop effective strategies for adding numbers together without using the skyscraper.

Hand out Student Sheet 4, Many Changes to Make +2, and read the questions with students. Working individually, students use as many Changes Cards as they can from one set of 20 cards to make a net change of +2. Students fill in the sheet as they finish the activity.

Look for the following points in students' work:

- Are students using strategies, such as making combinations of opposites to use many changes, or are they laying out changes without planning and then counting to see if they work?
- Are students using a few or many cards? Challenge those who are using only a few to use more cards.

Name __Amanda__                    Date __Feb. 6__

## Many Changes to Make +2

Pick any changes you want from one whole deck of
Changes Cards. Make the longest set of changes that
gives you a net change of +2.

Then answer these questions:

What cards did you use?

+2 +2 +2 -2 -2 +3 +3 +3 -3 -3 -3 00 +1 +1 +1 -1 -1 -1 -1

What card or cards did you *not* use?

-2

Explain why the cards you did not use would not work
to make a net change of +2.

Because -2 would take you back
to start.

Many students will use the maximum number of cards possible, 19, omit-
ting one of the –2 cards. Students who work slowly and use fewer cards
may not be using opposites and may not consider that in the whole deck of
Changes Cards, the net change is zero.

All students should be able to use more than two changes to make a net change;
they should be able to compute the net change of a set of three or four changes.

# Sessions 3 and 4 Follow-Up

**Playing the Game of Many Changes at Home** In order to play the game at
home, students will need two copies of the Changes Cards (a deck for each
player); Student Sheet 2, Net Change with Many Changes; Student Sheet 3,
How to Play the Game of Many Changes; and one set of Net Change Cards.
They will also need the Skyscraper that was already sent home for homework.

 **Homework**

If students do not have scissors at home, allow them some time before the
end of the day to color the back of the Changes Cards and the Net Change
Cards sheets and to cut out the sets of cards to take home.

# DIALOGUE BOX

## Making a Net Change of –4

In this discussion, which occurs during the activity Finding Many Ways to Make a Net Change (p. 14), the students are sharing their ideas for different sets of changes that make the same net change, in this case –4.

**Here's a harder one to do. I'm starting on 6 and ending on 2. Tell me a way to do it with three changes.**

Seung: Down 3, up 2, down 3.

*[Tries it out]* **What net change is this?**

Amanda: Minus 4.

**Who has another way to make a net change of minus four?**

Dylan: Up 2, down 3, down 3.

**Another?**

Ricardo: Minus 3, minus 3, plus 2.

Dylan: It's the same as mine, but a different order.

Amanda: We had that one too, but in a different order.

**Can you make minus 4 with more than three changes?**

Ricardo: Minus 3, minus 3, plus 2, zero.

**That's a good one! Can anyone do four changes without zero?**

Jamal: Plus 1, plus 1, minus 2, minus 4.

**Is minus 4 okay? We have no cards with minus 4.**

Jennifer: Yes! And I've got another one. Plus 1, plus 1, plus 1, minus 7.

Some classes decide to allow only one zero to be used; otherwise, when the number of changes is specified, the task is too easy. Others decide to include numbers higher than +3 and lower than –3. These students are moving beyond the limits of the numbers on the Changes Cards and the floors on the skyscraper diagram. One sign of this is that they are naming the changes as numbers without mentioning the elevator floors.

# Thirty Changes

## What Happens

Students post a sequence of 30 changes along a wall. Working in groups, they find out what the total or net effect of applying all the changes would be. They use strategies they have learned, such as –2 cancels +2, so if they count three –2's and five +2's, they know they need to consider only the extra two +2's. Students' work focuses on:

- developing strategies for adding a long sequence of changes
- keeping track of partial calculations

### Materials

- Pad of stick-on notes
- Student Sheet 5 ( 1 per student, homework)
- Calculators

## Activity

### Where Does the Elevator End Up?

Students work in groups of four. Each group chooses four to seven changes from –3 to +3 to write on stick-on notes and display. (The total number of changes for the whole class should be about 30. You might ask the students how many each group should pick to have this total.)

Students put their sets of changes up on the wall at eye level so that all the stick-on notes are in one long line going horizontally across the wall or the board.

Each group organizes its members to figure out where an elevator would end up if it started at zero (the ground floor) and moved according to all the posted changes. They make sure each student has a job to do. The group is responsible for:

- knowing each member's task
- keeping track of their work on paper
- checking their answer
- explaining how they got their answer and how they checked it

**Note:** Do not find the answer ahead of your students. We feel this is critical to the success of this activity. In the follow-up discussion, the students are to *convince* you of their answer. Your role is to listen to their ideas and to sincerely question when you are unsure of their accuracy or of their strategies.

**Discussing the Results**  When the groups are finished, bring the class together to compare their strategies. Groups present their answers and their methods, comparing and defending answers if there are differences.

Students may think of using a calculator to check the net change. Those who do this report their findings to the class so the calculator-generated answer can be evaluated along with the others. Discuss with your students the experience of using the calculator on a problem like this.

**Did using a calculator make it easier to find the answer?**

After comparing strategies and noticing that some are much more efficient than others, students may want to try another problem. They can put up another set of 30 (or more) changes and find the net change.

---

## Using Bigger Mixed-Up Changes

In this activity, students write their own problems similar to those they have been doing mentally in the Ten-Minute Math activity (as described on p. 13). They may use any numbers they want, as long as they use larger numbers (farther from zero) than are on the Changes Cards.

Students write a set of five or six changes that has a small net change, recording the changes in a mixed-up order that makes it difficult to figure out the net change. Then they write the same changes in an order that makes it easy to figure out the net change. They show how they would figure out the net change from the easy order.

For example, these changes have a net change of +2:

+29 +2 −38 −300 +11 +298

It is easier to see this if we reorder the numbers this way:

+2 +298 −300 +29 +11 −38

Then, combining changes:

+300 −300 +40 −38

0 +2 = +2

---

## Session 5 Follow-Up

 **Homework**

**Mixed-Up Changes**  After Session 5, send home Student Sheet 5, Mixed-Up Changes. Students solve a mixed-up changes problem and make up one more using larger numbers. As they did in class, they write down the changes in a mixed-up order and then show how they would change the order to make the problem easier. Collect these problems from students to use as mental arithmetic problems throughout this unit in the continuing Ten-Minute Math activity.

# Missing Information Problems

## What Happens

Students solve changes problems in which critical information is missing: either the starting point or one or more of the changes. They write about their strategies for finding a missing starting floor. Students' work focuses on:

■ generating effective strategies for solving a number problem in which one piece of information is missing

■ generating effective strategies for finding possibilities when two pieces of information are missing

■ organizing answers to discover if they have found all possible solutions

## Materials

■ Skyscraper transparency or diagram

■ Stick-on notes

■ Students' skyscrapers

■ Game pieces (10 per student)

■ Sets of Changes Cards (from earlier sessions)

■ Student Sheet 6 (2 per pair, plus extras)

■ Student Sheet 7 (1 per student)

---

**Finding a Missing Change** Make up a trip and write the numbers that describe it next to your skyscraper (transparency or diagram). Plan the starting place, two changes, and the ending place, but leave out one of the changes for your students to figure out. Present the problem:

**Yesterday I went on a trip in the elevator. I started on floor 4 at the [art studio]. Then I pushed another button, and after that I pushed –2. I ended up on floor B1 at the [pizza parlor]. What button did I push before –2 to get there? What places did I visit?**

As you tell the story of the trip, write down the numbers and indicate missing numbers with a box or question mark.

| Starting Floor | Changes | Ending Floor |
|---|---|---|
| 4 | ?   –2 | B1 |

Allow students a minute or two to work in pairs on the solution to this problem. Encourage them to use their skyscrapers if they wish. Then call on some pairs to share their solutions—both the answer they got and an explanation of why they think it is correct.

## Activity

## Missing Starts and Missing Changes

**Finding a Missing Start**    Present a problem that omits the starting place, such as the following one:

**I got into my elevator and pushed the +2 button. After this I pushed the −3 button. When I got out of my elevator, I was on floor 1 at the [library]. What floor did I start on?**

| Starting Floor | Changes | Ending Floor |
|:---:|:---:|:---:|
| ? | +2  −3 | 1 |

Allow students a few minutes to solve this problem. Then ask them to share their strategies. See the **Teacher Note,** Solving Back-in-Time Problems (p. 26), for an explanation of typical student approaches to this type of backward problem.

## Our Own Missing Information Problems

Distribute Student Sheet 6, Missing Information Problems, to pairs of students. Point out that the sheet has places for names of the problem creators and the problem solvers.

Two pairs of students work together. Each pair creates two or three trips with either the starting number or one of the changes missing. They vary the position of the missing number. Then the two pairs exchange papers, solve each other's problems, and then explain their solutions to each other.

When both pairs of students in a group have solved the problems posed by the other pair, they make up another set of two or three problems for each other to solve. When they have done four or five problems, each pair chooses a problem they thought was difficult. At the bottom of Student Sheet 6, they describe the strategy they used to solve it.

❖ **Tip for the Linguistically Diverse Classroom**   Instead of writing about how they solved a difficult problem, students can copy the problem, then show their strategy using numbers and symbols. For example:

Starting Floor: ?        Changes: +3  −2 −1 +2
Ending Floor: B2
B2 −2 = B4
B4 +1 = B3
B3 +2 = B1
B1 −3 = B4
Starting Floor: = B4

As students are working on these problems, help the groups who are having difficulty and take note of the different approaches students are using to solve the problems. Encourage those who find the Back-in-Time problems difficult to stay with this kind of problem in order to understand it better. As students seem ready, suggest that they work with more changes.

**Discussing Strategies for Missing Information Problems**   Once everyone has had some experience with these problems, have a brief discussion of strategies so students may learn from each other. You might ask them which kinds of problems they found most challenging and which they found easiest. What strategies did they use to solve the hardest ones? See the **Dialogue Box**, Finding a Missing Start (p. 28), for one example of a discussion of strategies.

## More Than One Piece Missing

Some students may be ready to go on to problems in which two pieces of information are missing. They now start with a new copy of Student Sheet 6 and exchange problems with another pair who are doing the same kind of problem. Students who are not ready for this will continue to investigate problems with one missing number, as in the preceding activity.

When more than one piece of information is missing, there are many possible solutions. For example, a two-change trip starting at 3 and ending at 1 can be solved with –2 0, or –1 –1, or –3 +1.

If any size change were allowed, the number of solutions would be infinite. However, when we confine the changes to the seven possibilities on the cards (–3 to +3), there is always a finite number of solutions. This means that certain problems have no solution. For example, using the Changes Cards, there is no way of traveling from 1 to 10 in two changes. To distinguish among problems with no solution, with one solution, or with many solutions is an important aspect of this exploration.

One challenge these problems present for students is finding all the possible answers. As you observe students, you may want to raise questions like these:

**How many solutions are there that work for this problem? Do you have all the ways? How can you know if you have found all the ways?**

## Assessment

## Six Changes and a Missing Start

Distribute Student Sheet 7, Six Changes and a Missing Start, and read the two problems aloud for students.

Students may use their skyscrapers to solve these problems if they wish. For some ideas about evaluating student responses, see the **Teacher Note**, Assessment: Six Changes and a Missing Start (p. 27).

## *Solving Back-in-Time Problems*                    > Teacher Note

When a problem gives the changes and an ending floor, but no starting floor, students must approach the problem backwards. Most students use one of two ways to solve these backward problems.

A few students figure out they can use *opposites*. For example:

Ending floor: 3
Changes: –2 +1 –3

Student's observation: "It ended at 3 after minusing 3, so before that it must have been at 6. Before it went plus 1 it must have been at 5. And first it did minus 2, so before that it was at 7. It started at 7."

The strategy here is to start at the ending number, 3, then add what was subtracted and subtract what was added:

$$3 + 3 - 1 + 2 = 7$$

Many students use *trial and adjust*. That is, they pick a starting floor as a guess and move according to the changes to see if it comes out right. If it doesn't end up on the right floor, some students randomly guess at a new starting floor to try. Others select their next try based on their error. Thus, if the floor they end on is too high, they try a new starting floor a little lower. They continue to try starting floors until they find one that leads to the target ending place.

One common incorrect strategy is to start with the end number and apply the changes in reverse order without changing the signs. For the example given above, this would put the student at –1:

$$3 - 3 + 1 - 2 = -1$$

Whatever strategies students use, ask them to check their answers by beginning with the number they think is the start and then using the changes to see if they get the correct ending number.

# Assessment: Six Changes and a Missing Start

Student Sheet 7 presents students with two assessment tasks. In problem 1, they are asked to find six changes that would take them from 4 to 3.

Students with a strong understanding of net change are likely to be systematic in generating their combinations of numbers, juxtaposing a number and its opposite. For example, consider this solution:

+3 –3 +3 –3   0 –1

This student considered how a number and its opposite cancel each other.

Here's another solution:

+1 +2 –3 –1 +1 –1

This student's choice of +1 +2 followed by –3 reflects an understanding of how two changes added together can be undone by the opposite of their sum.

Students with a less strong understanding of net change may not use a systematic way of generating their numbers, or they may not be able to come up with three combinations that work. For example:

–1 +3 –1 – 1 +1 –2

This solution is correct, but it took the student a long time to generate it by trial and error moving along the elevator track.

Other students may use fewer than six changes, or the combinations that they generate may not be accurate. For example, one student gave these three combinations:

+1 +1 –1 –1 +1 +2

–1 +1 –1 +1 –1 +1

–2 –2 +1 +1 –2 +3

Only the last combination is a solution to the problem.

For problem 2, students are asked to find a missing start. Students with a strong understanding are likely to use either an opposites strategy or a trial-and-adjust strategy (as explained in the **Teacher Note**, Solving Back-in-Time Problems, p. 26.)

The explanations below are examples of using the opposites strategy:

> I figured out the net change was –2 and changed the minus into a plus and used that on the 4. (This student got the correct answer, 6.)

> I added –3 –1 and got –4, and –4 and +2 equal –2. So the starting floor is 2 above the ending floor (This student also got the correct answer, 6.)

Another student successfully used the trial-and-adjust strategy in response to the result she got on the first try:

> First I started at 5 but it was too little, so I tried 6 and it worked.

A student with somewhat less understanding might try out a lot of numbers, but will not use the feedback from one result to come up with the next try. The explanations below are examples:

> First I started on the 0, then on the 1 and 2 and 3 and 4 and 5. They didn't work. And then I started on the 6, and it worked.

> I did trial and error. I first did 8 then 7, and 6. Then I got my answer. It was 6.

Students who have not yet developed an understanding of these problems are apt to start with the end number and apply the changes without changing the signs. The explanation below is an example.

> I figured it out because if you end on 4 and if you took a –3 you would be on the 1, and if you got +2 then you would be on the 3, and then –1, so you would be on the 2.

# DIALOGUE BOX

## Finding a Missing Start

In this discussion during the Missing Starts and Missing Changes activity (p. 23), the teacher posed a problem with a missing start and then asked students to talk about how they solved it. The changes were –3 –2. The elevator ended at floor 9.

**Mark:** I tried starting with 4, I did 3 down, then 2 more down. It came down here (below zero) so I knew that was wrong.

**What did you do next?**

**Mark:** I tried a higher number. I did some different numbers. When I started with 14, it worked.

**Maria:** We changed minuses to pluses.

**Rashad** (Maria's partner): We got 14 because we did 9 plus 3 plus 2. Because if a number minuses it, the same number has to be added.

**Maria:** Because you subtract, but you're starting at the end so you have to add.

**Rashad:** You have to put –3 to +3 and –2 to +2 and add them all up.

**Does everyone understand the backward way?**

**Several students:** No.

**Yoshi:** I did it sort of the same way. You end at floor 9 and you did down 2. Before you did down 2, you were at floor 11. Before that, you did down 3 so you started at 3 higher. 11 plus 3—14.

**Chantelle:** Yes. You did down 5 altogether. You started at 5 higher than 9, so you started at 14.

These students demonstrate different ways of solving the problem. Mark uses trial and error. Yoshi narrates the problem backward, a step at a time. Maria, Rashad, and perhaps Chantelle find the net change and then add its opposite.

# Stopping at Many Floors

## What Happens

Students play a game in which they arrange a set of changes to make the elevator stop on as many different floors as they can. Students' work focuses on:

- recognizing that different orders of the same changes can take you to different intermediate places

- recognizing that a number followed by its opposite takes you back to the same floor

## Materials

- Students' skyscrapers
- Chips (10 per student)
- Paper and pencils
- Sets of Changes Cards (from earlier sessions)
- Transparency of Student Sheet 8 (optional)
- Student Sheet 8 (1 per pair or group and 1 per student for homework)
- Student Sheet 9 (1 per student, homework)

## Pick Up Chips

**Introducing the Game**  The object of this game is to make the elevator in the skyscraper stop at as many different floors as possible. Distribute chips and make sure students have their skyscrapers and Changes Cards. Tell them to place chips on ten numbers in a row on their skyscrapers.

Play one round together as a class. Draw four Changes Cards from a set and write the changes on the board, for example, +3 +1 −1 +2. Students take out the corresponding Changes Cards and try to arrange them so as to direct the elevator to stop at as many different floors as possible.

Players pick up the chip at the starting floor they choose and then, moving from floor to floor according to their order of changes, pick up a chip at each new floor where they stop. It doesn't matter which floor they start on, but it tends to work best if they begin on a floor near the middle of the ones they have covered with chips.

In the example above (+3 +1 −1 +2), if an elevator started on floor 0 and moved according to the changes in that order, it would go to floor 3, floor 4, back to floor 3, and then to floor 5. The player would pick up a chip for the starting floor and then additional chips for floors 3, 4, and 5—four chips in all. However, with the arrangement +3 +1 +2 −1, a player would collect five chips, one for 0 and one each for floors 3, 4, 6, and 5. A player would also pick up five chips with this arrangement: +1 +3 −1 +2 (for floors 0, 1, 4, 3, and 5).

Record on the transparency of Student Sheet 8 (or on the board) the different arrangements students found for the given set of changes, and the number of different floors on which each arrangement directs the elevator to stop. Some students may notice that reversing the order of an arrangement results in the same number of different floors.

If students are not yet clear about how to play this game, try another example as a class.

**Note:** The greatest number of floors possible for one set of changes is one more than the number of changes, because the starting floor is counted. However, it is not always possible to pick up the maximum number of chips with a particular set of changes. When zero is among the changes, it will never be possible to pick up the maximum number of chips.

**Playing the Game**   Hand out Student Sheet 8, the recording sheet for Pick Up Chips, to pairs or small groups. Students take turns picking the four Changes Cards to start a round of play. They work out each new set of changes on their individual skyscrapers, then discuss and record their solutions. While students are playing, move from group to group and ask questions like these:

**What kinds of number combinations make the elevator stop at as many floors as possible? What orders of numbers should you stay away from?**

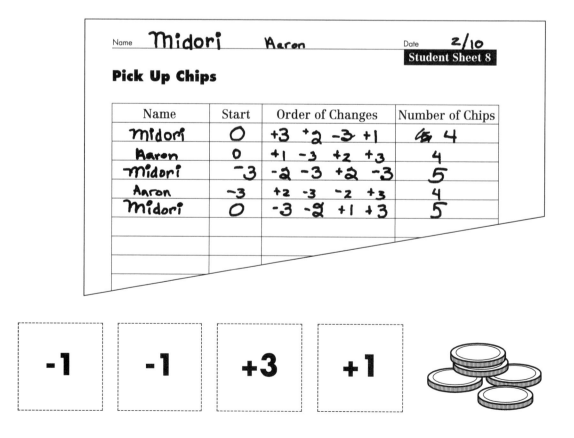

Name **Midori** Aaron          Date **2/10**
**Student Sheet 8**

**Pick Up Chips**

| Name | Start | Order of Changes | Number of Chips |
|------|-------|------------------|-----------------|
| Midori | 0 | +3  +2  -3  +1 | ~~5~~ 4 |
| Aaron | 0 | +1  -3  +2  +3 | 4 |
| Midori | ‾3 | -2  -3  +2  -3 | 5 |
| Aaron | ‾3 | +2  -3  ‾2  +3 | 4 |
| Midori | 0 | -3  -2  +1  +3 | 5 |
| | | | |
| | | | |
| | | | |

-1     -1     +3     +1

# Session 8 Follow-Up

**Playing Pick Up Chips at Home**  Hand out Student Sheet 8, Pick Up Chips, and Student Sheet 9, How to Play Pick Up Chips. Students should already have skyscrapers and Changes Cards at home to play the game with family or friends.

**Homework**

**Fewest Floors**  Students can play the variation of Pick Up Chips in which they arrange each combination of changes to stop the elevator at the *fewest* different floors possible. The goal, then, is to pick up as few chips as possible.

**Extensions**

**A Picture of the Game**  Students draw a diagram of one round of Pick Up Chips and write a description of how they worked out that round. This is good preparation for the activities in the next investigation, where students will be finding ways to graph or map their elevator trips.

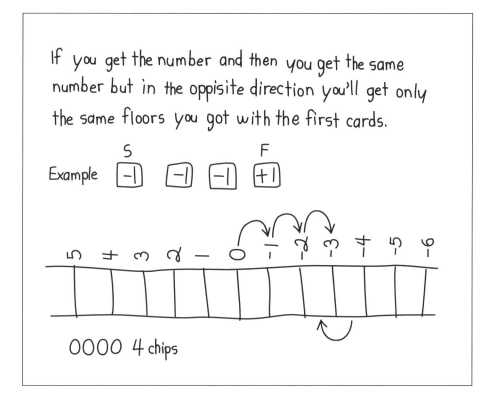

# Representing Elevator Trips

## What Happens

**Session 1: Graphing Elevator Trips**  Students think of a secret elevator trip and represent it graphically in a form of their choice. They exchange these graphs/maps with each other to be sure they are clear. They revise their representations as necessary and make final drafts for display and discussion.

**Sessions 2 and 3: Repeating Elevator Trips** Students look at graphs that show change over time and discuss what they observe. Then they graph a sequence of three to five changes and extend the graph to see what it would look like if the same changes were repeated over and over again.

**Session 4: Plus and Minus Graphs**  Students make graphs that follow one of several sequences of pluses and minuses. They group the graphs according to plus-and-minus sequence and determine what the graphs in each group have in common.

## Mathematical Emphasis

- Representing numbers graphically
- Interpreting changes in direction on a graph
- Understanding how the passage of time is represented on graphs showing change over time
- Finding net change on graphs
- Comparing overall shapes of graphs

## What to Plan Ahead of Time

### Materials

- Plain paper (Sessions 1–3)
- Crayons, colored pencils, or markers (Sessions 1–3)
- Tape (Sessions 2–3)
- Overhead projector (Sessions 2–3)

### Other Preparation

- Duplicate student sheets and teaching resources (located at the end of this unit) in the following quantities. If you have Student Activity Booklets, copy only the items marked with an asterisk, including any transparencies needed.

*For Session 1*

One-centimeter graph paper (p. 76): 4–6 per student, to be used throughout the investigation

Student Sheet 10, Change-Over-Time Graphs (p. 72): 1 per student (homework)

*For Sessions 2–3*

Graphs Showing Change Over Time (p. 77): 1 transparency*

Repeating Elevator Graphs (p. 78): 1 transparency*

*For Session 4*

Student Sheet 11, Plus and Minus Graphs (p. 73): 1 per student

Student Sheet 12, Repeating Elevator Problem (p. 74): 1 per student

Student Sheet 13, Net Change on a Graph (p. 75): 1 per student (homework)

Small Plus and Minus Cards* (p. 79): enough for each student to receive one card (there are six cards on the sheet). Cut apart these cards.

Large Plus and Minus Cards* (p. 80). Cut on dotted lines.

- Collect graphs (perhaps from the newspaper) that show change over time, moving from left to right across the page. (Sessions 2–3)

# Graphing Elevator Trips

## Materials

- One-centimeter graph paper (1–2 per student)
- Plain paper
- Crayons, colored pencils, or markers
- Student Sheet 10 (1 per student for homework)

## What Happens

Students think of a secret elevator trip and represent it graphically in a form of their choice. They exchange these graphs/maps with each other to be sure they are clear. They revise their representations as necessary and make final drafts for display and discussion. Students' work focuses on:

- representing numbers graphically
- constructing their own representations of changes

 **Ten-Minute Math: Estimation and Number Sense** Three or four times before the end of the unit, do some more Estimation and Number Sense activities outside of math time. Start to use larger numbers. Some possible problems:

$$80 + 1400 - 15 \qquad\qquad 2500 + 4 - 300$$

$$25 + 650 + 500 - 75 \qquad 305 + 140 + 496$$

Show the problem for a minute or less; then cover it. Students do the problem mentally to find the answer or a good estimate. Poll students for their answers. Reveal the problem again and ask students to share their solution strategies. Students then check the problem with calculators. For full instructions and variations, see pp. 55–56.

---

## Activity

### Inventing Ways to Represent Trips

Introduce the making of elevator graphs/maps:

Up until now, we have been describing elevator trips with numbers, or by telling the story of the trip in words. What if you wanted to show this trip in a different way—by drawing its path on a graph? Think about how you could show the path of this trip so someone else could follow it.

Plan a mystery elevator trip with a starting floor and three or four changes. Make your plan in secret. Then make a graph of your trip. Try not to use any words. Think of a way to show where your trip starts and ends and where it goes in between. Someone else should be able to understand the trip just by looking at your graph. Make a draft first. Then exchange it with someone to find out if it's clear.

Have both graph paper and plain paper available. At this point, students work for only about 10 minutes. Emphasize that the final graphs today need only be clear, not polished. Observe the students' work to see if you can understand the trips their graphs show. Provide feedback by telling students where you think their trips go. If it is unclear, for example, where a trip starts, point that out. See the **Teacher Note**, Students' Graphs of Elevator Trips (p. 36), for examples of approaches students have taken.

**Interpreting Each Other's Graphs**  As students finish their drafts, they exchange them with other students. They try to tell the whole story of each other's trip or act out the trip on their skyscraper. The interpreter should be able to tell on what floor the trip starts, where the elevator goes in correct order, and on what floor the trip ends. If the interpreter can't read the trip as the author intended, the author and interpreter figure out together what can be done to make the graph clearer.

**Making Final Drafts**  Once students have decided how to clarify their graphs based on feedback from the interpreter, they make a final copy that can be seen by other students when it is displayed at the front of the room. They may do this by darkening their rough draft graph or by redrawing it larger, for example. As students work, choose an example of each distinct type of graph that they make to feature in a discussion.

---

**Activity**

**Discussing the Graphs**

Display the graphs you have picked out so that everyone can see them. Challenge students to figure out where the trips represented in these graphs start and where they go. Before discussing each graph, you might ask students to write down the trip they think it represents. Then ask the students how they figured out the trip from the graph.

**How do you know where the trip started and ended? How do you know what order to go in?**

To include students whose graphs are not displayed, ask who made their graphs in a similar way and if anyone has a suggestion to help the creator of the displayed graph clarify the information presented.

---

**Session 1 Follow-Up**

**Change-Over-Time Graphs**  Ask students to look in newspapers, books, and other sources for graphs that show something changing over time. You might show some examples, like graphs of temperatures, average heights of children as they grow, or increasing population. Students record what they find (and where they found it) on Student Sheet 10, Change-Over-Time Graphs. What students bring in will be shared in the next session.

 **Homework**

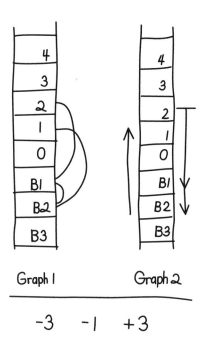

Graph 1          Graph 2

-3   -1   +3

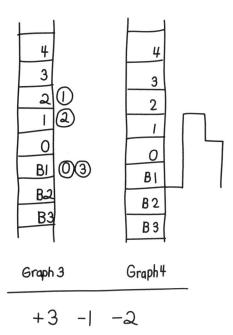

Graph 3          Graph 4

+3   -1   -2

Many students visualize an elevator trip as a series of vertical moves. Consequently, they tend to draw a number of arrows up and down, staying in a vertical column. The four graphs illustrated above are examples of what third graders have drawn to show elevator trips.

Graphs 1 and 2 show this trip: Start on floor 2, then move −3, −1, +3, and end on floor 1.

It is difficult to tell from Graph 1 where the start is or in what order the elevator traveled to each of the different floors. Students solve this problem in different ways. In Graph 2, the student has made clear the start and order by drawing a firm line at the start and adding arrows. If the trip were longer or more complicated, it might become difficult to tell the order of the changes.

Graphs 3 and 4 show this trip: Start on floor B1 and move +3, − 1, −2.

In Graph 3, notice how the start is marked with zero and each stop is numbered to show what floors to go to in order. In Graph 4, the lines move from left to right to show the order of the changes.

Graph 1 needs some editing to make it clearer. All the other graphs shown here are fine for this task. Although Graph 4 is the closest to a conventional graph, it seemed odd to the other third grade students in the class where it was made. The students tried to see it as a picture, and they wondered if it depicted more than one skyscraper, or if you had to cross the floor at each level to take a new elevator.

Do not insist that students make a conventional graph for this session. The criterion for a successful graph here is that someone else can interpret the intended elevator trip correctly.

It is important to encourage your students to think for themselves about how to represent something that takes place over time. The experience they gain constructing graphs for themselves is likely to increase their understanding of more conventional graphs, which will be introduced in the next session. At that time, they will view graphs that show change over time moving from left to right across the page. They will use that model to make graphs of longer trips.

# Repeating Elevator Trips

## What Happens

Students look at graphs that show change over time and discuss what they observe. Then they graph a sequence of three to five changes and extend the graph to see what it would look like if the same changes were repeated over and over again. Student work focuses on:

- representing numbers graphically
- understanding that a "going up" graph indicates a positive change, a "going down" graph indicates a negative change, and a horizontal graph indicates zero change
- recognizing that passage of time or order of events can be represented by moving from left to right
- finding net change on graphs

## Materials

- All materials from Session 1
- Collected sample graphs
- Transparency of Graphs Showing Change Over Time
- Transparency of Repeating Elevator Graphs
- Overhead projector
- Tape

---

In the main activity in these sessions, Graphing Repeating Trips (p. 40), students graph elevator trips that represent a set of changes that repeat indefinitely. They will need a clear way to show a series of changes over time. To gather some ideas of how to do this, they look at the transparency, Graphs Showing Change Over Time.

**Where does the story on each of these graphs begin? How can you tell? Where does it end? What on the graph helps you decide what order things happened in?**

**On the second graph, what do you think it means when the line goes higher and lower? What is it showing?**

Distribute the other graphs that you and the students collected so that every student or group of students can look at one. Students discuss in small groups how to read the story of the graph or graphs, using the questions above as a guide.

Bring students together to sum up their observations. Ask them what different things a peak (a line at its highest point) shows on these graphs. Make a list of all the ideas. Then ask students to name other things we might show changing on a graph. Some ideas might include speeds, heights, ages, amounts of money, weights, temperatures.

## Graphs That Show Change Over Time

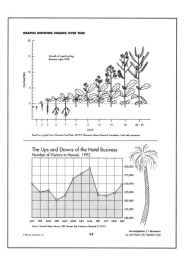

Conclude the viewing of the graphs with the following idea:

**Just as we read words on a page from left to right, we also read graphs from left to right. That way, even without seeing the word *start*, the viewer knows where to begin reading.**

**Teacher Checkpoint**

## Graphing a Set of Changes

**Introducing Repeating Elevator Graphs**   Tell students that you have another story about an elevator.

**You are taking a trip in your elevator. When you push the first button, the elevator goes where you have sent it. The next few buttons you push also take you to where you want to go. However, when you push another button, the elevator starts to repeat the whole set of changes again, and again, and again. It is on a repeat cycle and it cannot stop!**

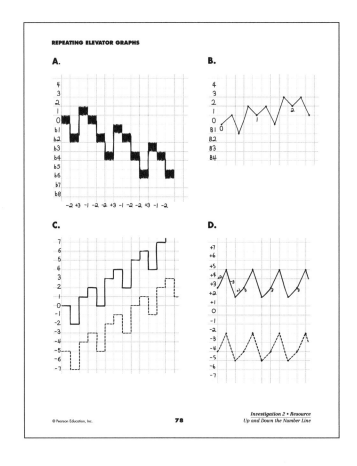

Show the transparency of Repeating Elevator Graphs. These are graphs that students in different classes have used to represent the repeating elevator. Show one graph at a time, giving students a chance to figure out how it was made and to read the floors and changes it represents.

Note: In Graph A, the whole floor is filled in. In Graph B, dots are put in the middle of each floor and then joined by lines. In Graph C, a line is drawn across the floor and then up or down to show the next change. In Graph D, dots are placed on consecutive vertical lines to show the floors, with lines drawn to connect the dots. (Graphs C and D show the same pattern from more than one starting point, which students will be doing in the next activity.)

Point out to students that the graphs show the repeating patterns clearly. The graphs may be read from left to right, and they use only one line or column for each new change. On all the graphs, there is a new elevator shaft for each change of floors.

**Graphing Many Changes**   Students use one-centimeter graph paper for this activity. They may tape pieces of graph paper together, adding new sheets above, below, or to the right as needed. Students each choose three to five changes and write these on their graph paper as a title. Then they construct a graph that starts on floor 0 and shows the trip an elevator would make if it followed that sequence of changes.

Note: Some teachers choose one format that they think their students will feel comfortable using. Others let individual students decide which format to use. Whatever you decide, all students should make graphs that move from left to right across the page to show the repeating elevator trip.

As students work on the first set of changes, observe to be sure that they graph in a way they can easily repeat, and that they are using only one column for each change. It is typical for students to move two spaces to the right as well as two spaces up when they show a change of +2, or three spaces to the right as well as three spaces down to show –3.

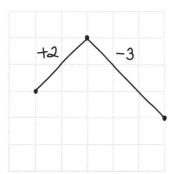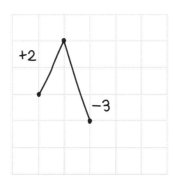

# Graphing Repeating Trips

Student does this:                              instead of this:

When students have graphed their set of changes once and you have checked it, they use another color to extend their graph to show what the trip would look like if the sequence of changes were repeated. They continue to show the repeating pattern, using a different color for each repeat. They begin each new repeat where the previous one finished.

After students complete three or four repeats of the set of changes, they write on the graph the number of the first starting floor and of the starting floor for each repeat.

**Starting the Trip on Another Floor**   On the same paper, students make a graph of the same repeating changes, this time starting on another floor. They make two or three graphs, each time starting on a different floor, using different colors or lines (dotted, dashed) for contrast. (See Graphs C and D on Repeating Elevator Graphs for examples.)

Again, when students finish each of these graphs, they write the number of the first starting floor as well as the starting floor of each repeat.

# Analyzing the Graphs

Students post their graphs where everyone can see them. You might group the graphs according to whether they go up and up (have a positive net change), down and down (have a negative net change), or keep coming back to the place they start (have a net change of zero). Give students some time to look at them.

Write some questions on the board for students to think about and discuss with their partners. Here are some possibilities:

**What patterns do you notice in the shapes of the graphs? What patterns did you notice when you listed the floors where each repeat starts? Why do you think these patterns are there?**

**How can you tell where the elevator starts to repeat?**

**Is the net change of anyone's set of changes zero? How can you tell? Which graphs have a positive or "plus" net change? Which ones have a negative or "minus" net change?**

In a brief discussion, students share some of the patterns they see and their reasoning about why the patterns occur. Point out how the net change of the set of changes repeats again and again. For example, in a graph of changes with a net change of +4, the first set of changes will start at 0 and go to floor 4. The first repeat will start at floor 4 and go to floor 8. The next repeat will go to floor 12. When the pattern starts on a different floor, it will still add four floors in each repeat.

❖ **Tip for the Linguistically Diverse Classroom**    Instead of writing questions on the board for discussion, state them orally in a way that lets students list or draw their answers. For example:
**Show the graphs that go up and up.**
**Show the graphs that go down and down.**
**Show the graphs with zero net change.**
**Draw some of the patterns you see on the different graphs.**
**Show which patterns might go together.**

# Sessions 2 and 3 Follow-Up

**Up and Up, Down and Down**   Students think of sets of changes that, if repeated, would make graphs that go up and up, go down and down, or keep coming back to where they start. Put these headings on the board: Up and Up, Down and Down, Return to Starting Place. Students generate a number of sets of changes for each category.

**Extension**

# Plus and Minus Graphs

## Materials

- One-centimeter graph paper
- Small Plus and Minus Cards (1 card per student)
- Large Plus and Minus Cards
- Student Sheet 11 (1 per student)
- Student Sheet 12 (1 per student)
- Student Sheet 13 (1 per student, homework)

## What Happens

Students make graphs that follow one of several sequences of pluses and minuses. They group the graphs according to sequence and determine what the graphs in each group have in common. Student work focuses on:

- comparing overall shapes of graphs
- relating going up with positive change, going down with negative change, and staying level with zero change

## Activity

### Introducing Plus and Minus Graphs

See the **Teacher Note**, Graphs of Plus and Minus Sequences (p. 45), for information to help with this activity. Start by putting the following sequence of pluses, minuses, and zeros on the board:

$$+ + - - 0$$

**Let's say that this is all the information we have about where the elevator goes. We don't know the exact floors the elevator stops on, but this sequence of pluses, minuses, and zeros gives us important information.**

Have someone suggest in words and a sketch what a graph that follows this sequence might look like.

**Does anyone have another way of sketching it? After which change is it at the highest point? the lowest point?**

**Could the lowest point be at the start? Name a set of changes that would put the lowest point at the start. Name a set of changes that would put the lowest point at the end.**

Lowest point at start
+3 +2 −1 −2  0

Lowest point at end
+1 +1 −2 −2  0

## Making Plus and Minus Graphs

You are going to make graphs from a series of changes that are only pluses, minuses, and zeros. You will receive a piece of paper with some pluses and minuses on it. Don't show it to anyone. Make a graph that follows your sequence. Work alone on this.

Distribute graph paper and one Small Plus and Minus Card to each student. Be sure students know that they should represent the pluses and minuses in exactly the order in which they appear on the card. Give students a few minutes to work on their graphs. Ask students to put a star or the word *top* at the top of their graph so that graphs will be oriented properly later.

While students are working, cut apart the six Large Plus and Minus Cards and post them across the board or the wall as headings for the next activity.

When everyone has finished, collect all the graphs.

Hand out Student Sheet 11, Plus and Minus Graphs. This sheet shows the same six sequences of pluses and minuses that appear on the cards from which students have been working. Students sketch all six sequences down the right side. Give students just a few minutes to do this. They will use these sketches in the next activity.

## Matching Graphs

Mix up the single plus and minus graphs that students made in the preceding activity and pass them out again, one to each student, making sure that no one gets his or her own graph.

Students work in pairs to figure out which plus and minus sequences their two graphs belong to. Then they post each graph under the correct plus and minus heading on the board or wall.

When all the graphs have been posted, students check to be sure that all are in the right place. Students can compare the plus and minus sketches they made on Student Sheet 11 with the graphs being posted on the board.

Look at each plus and minus sequence in turn and ask:

**What is the same about all the graphs that fit this set of pluses and minuses? How do you know all these graphs fit here?**

### Assessment

## Repeating Elevator Problem

Distribute Student Sheet 12, Repeating Elevator Problem. Read all the questions on the sheet with the students.

While students are working, observe and help them as necessary. It may be especially important to help students identify the set of changes that is repeated. Once they know this, the other questions will become easier.

This graphing assessment will be difficult for many third graders. Line graphing is typically not introduced until sixth or seventh grade. Even so, this is a good chance for you to observe what your students have learned in their introduction to line graphs.

## Session 4 Follow-Up

 **Homework**

**Net Change on a Graph**   After Session 4, students do Student Sheet 13, Net Change on a Graph. Students figure out net change in two different ways and show how they did it.

# Graphs of Plus and Minus Sequences

Working with a plus and minus sequence leads to the reading of a graph as a sequence of increases and decreases. The only aspect that gets specified is whether the graph goes up, goes down, or stays the same. Many different graphs can be made for + + − − 0; but for all of them, the overall shape goes up twice, then down twice, and then stays the same.

$$+ \ + \ - \ - \ 0$$

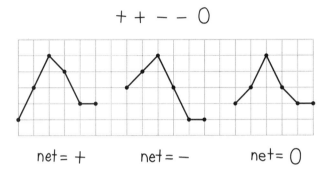

net = +        net = −        net = 0

Similarly, a − − + 0 − graph, no matter what the exact numbers are, would go down twice, then up, then stay in the same place before coming down again.

$$- \ - \ + \ 0 \ -$$

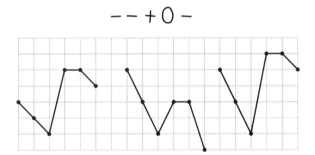

One of the most important aspects of graphs to learn is the shape of the graph—how it increases, decreases, or remains the same. The up/down/horizontal distinction provides information that is independent of height or steepness. For example, we may know when we reach the highest or the lowest floor just from the sequence of signs.

Anytime there is a change from + to −, the graph reaches a peak, and anytime there is a change from − to +, the graph shows a low point. When we have two peaks or low points, however, we cannot tell which is higher or lower without knowing the values of the changes. For example, given the sequence + + − − + + − −, we do not know if the highest point is after the second or the fourth plus.

Students have important intuitions about what "has to happen" with a given sequence of signs, and it is useful to explore these ideas.

# Inventing Board Games

## What Happens

**Session 1: Playing a Board Game** Students play a game in which moves are determined by Changes Cards. Two changes are picked randomly, and a third may be chosen by the player. The game is played on a horizontal track with negative space to the left and positive to the right.

**Sessions 2 and 3: Creating a Board Game** Students design their own games based on the number line, play them with other students, and revise them.

## Mathematical Emphasis

- Relating the direction of movement (left or right, up or down) to positive and negative numbers
- Using net change to determine an end point

## What to Plan Ahead of Time

### Materials

- Scissors: 1 per student (all sessions)
- Tape (all sessions)
- Chips or other game pieces in a variety of colors or shapes: 1 per student (all sessions)
- Interlocking cubes or other counters: 50 per student (all sessions, optional)
- Changes Cards from earlier investigations
- Crayons, colored pencils, or markers (all sessions)
- Calculators (all sessions)

### Other Preparation

- Assemble a sample Tiger Gameboard. Also draw the middle portion of the gameboard on the chalkboard to demonstrate the game. Play the game ahead of time by yourself or with a few students. (Session 1)
- To save class time, you may want to pre-assemble one Tiger Gameboard for each pair of students.

- Duplicate student sheets and teaching resources (located at the end of this unit) in the following quantities. If you have Student Activity Booklets, no copying is needed.

*For Session 1*

Tiger Gameboard (p. 83): 1 per pair, plus 1 per student for homework

Student Sheet 14, How to Play Save the Siberian Tiger (p. 82): 1 per pair, plus 1 per student for homework

Tiger Cards (p. 85): 1 set per pair, plus 1 set per student for homework. Cut up cards.

Changes Cards (p. 89): 1 set per student for homework

*For Sessions 2–3*

Make-Your-Own Gameboard (p. 87): 1 per student

# Playing a Board Game

### Materials

- Tiger Gameboard (1 per pair, plus 1 per student for homework, and pre-assembled sample)
- Student Sheet 14 (1 per pair, plus 1 per student for homework)
- Tiger Cards (1 set per pair, plus 1 set per student for homework)
- Skyscraper and Changes Cards from earlier investigations
- Scissors, tape
- Game pieces
- Calculators
- Stick-on notes
- Crayons, colored pencils, or markers

## What Happens

Students play a game in which moves are determined by Changes Cards. Two changes are picked randomly, and a third may be chosen by the player. The game is played on a horizontal track with negative space to the left and positive to the right. Students' work focuses on:

- relating the direction of movement (left or right, up or down) to positive and negative numbers
- using net change to determine an end point

---

**Activity**

## Save the Siberian Tiger

**Discussing the Gameboard** The board for this game is a long track laid down horizontally. Introduce this by holding up one of the student's sky-scrapers. Tell the students that you are going to turn it on its side to be a track for a game.

**Which way do you think I should rotate it? Should the positive numbers go to your right or to your left?**

Students are likely to agree with the convention of going from negative numbers at the left to positive numbers at the right. Tell students that this is something mathematicians agree on so that people won't get mixed up. For this game, negative numbers are labeled with the minus sign.

Show the prepared Tiger Gameboard so that numbers below zero are to the students' left and numbers above zero are to the right. Copy the center sections onto the chalkboard, including the penalties and rewards, perhaps up to space 5 or 6 in both positive and negative directions; use this to demonstrate how to play the game.

**Introducing the Game**  This game relates to saving the Siberian tiger from extinction. Share with students the information in the **Teacher Note,** About Siberian Tigers (p. 51). Read aloud the rewards and penalties in the game, which refer to some of the survival problems that Siberian tigers face and efforts being made by humans to save the tigers.

Explain that this is like a typical board game, in that players each move a game piece along a track. Instead of dice or a spinner, players use the Changes Cards to find out how many spaces and in what direction to move. Players gain or lose Tiger Cards as they play the game. The object of the game is to finish with the most Tiger Cards. Brief directions are given on Student Sheet 14, How to Play Save the Siberian Tiger.

To demonstrate the game, take six cards from a deck of Changes Cards: –3, –2, –1, +1, +2, +3 (one of each kind except 0). Place them face up in front of you. Explain that these are your CHOICE cards. Place the remainder in a stack face down; these are the CHANCE cards. Set up a Tiger Bank for the Tiger Cards. Place a stick-on note (your "game piece") on space 0, which is START.

Talk about what nearby space you would like to land on and what net change would get you there. Pick two face down CHANCE cards and show them to the class. Ask students to suggest a third card from your CHOICE cards (face up) that will move your piece to your target space. You can always choose *not* to use a CHOICE card if you like where the CHANCE cards take you. After you complete your move, if you gain or lose tigers, adjust your Tiger Cards accordingly. At the end of your turn, discard all the Changes Cards (CHOICE) that you used.

Point out that strategy is an important part of this game. Encourage students to first figure out which nearby space on the board they might move to and what net change would get them there. Also consider tradeoffs; that is, might it be worth losing 6 tigers (on space –8) for the chance to *double* your total tigers (on space –11)?

**Playing the Game** Distribute the following to each pair or group of three: one copy of the Tiger Gameboard, scissors, and tape; one copy of Student Sheet 14, How to Play Save the Siberian Tiger; and one set of Tiger Cards (2 sheets), or two sets for three players. Also make sure each player has a game piece distinct from the others.

Students first cut out and assemble their gameboard and cut apart the Tiger Cards, organizing them in piles by denomination. These are placed to the side in a Tiger Bank.

Players bring to their game their own sets of Changes Cards (from earlier investigations; each set should be colored or marked in some way so that sets can be easily restored after a game). Before the game, each player takes one of each different change (except 0) and spreads them out face up as CHOICE cards. All players mix their remaining Changes Cards together in a single deck and place it face down in the center as the CHANCE cards.

While students play, circulate to make sure they understand the rules. Clarify the following as necessary:

- Players adjust the number of tigers only at the end of each turn. They should pay no attention to spaces they touch in the middle of a turn.
- Players may return to a space again and again.
- If players are nearing either end of the gameboard and cannot move with the CHANCE cards they pick, they may use only a CHOICE card for that move. If they cannot move with any of their remaining CHOICE cards, they skip a turn.

As you see groups that do not seem to be using any strategy, help them consider alternatives as they plan their turns. Also see that they are able to make change from the bank as needed when gaining or losing Tiger Cards, and suggest that they "trade up" Tiger Cards (1's for 5's, 5's for 20's, and so on) to make them easier to count.

The game is over when the players have used all the CHANCE cards. Players total their Tiger Cards, and the one who has saved the most tigers is the winner.

# Session 1 Follow-Up

 **Homework**

**Playing Save the Siberian Tiger at Home** Students can take Save the Siberian Tiger home to play. They should each take a copy of the gameboard, the Tiger Cards, and How to Play Save the Siberian Tiger (Student Sheet 14). Students will also need the two sets of Changes Cards they took home during Investigation 1.

# About Siberian Tigers

As their name implies, Siberian tigers live in Siberia, which is located in Asia in the former USSR. Siberia extends from the Ural mountains in the west to the Pacific Ocean in the east. In the north it is bounded by the Arctic Ocean and in the south by China and Mongolia.

Tigers are the largest animals in the cat family—larger than lions, leopards, jaguars, and cheetahs—and the Siberian tiger is the largest cat of all. A typical adult male weighs about 400 pounds and measures 13 feet from its head to the end of its tail. A typical female weighs about 300 pounds.

Siberian tigers are well suited to the extreme cold in Siberia, where winter temperatures can reach −40 degrees Fahrenheit. Like all other kinds of tigers, Siberian tigers are generally nocturnal. Their prey consists of deer, elk, wild boars, bears, wolves, badgers, foxes, and occasionally salmon. In order to survive, they must eat about 300 pounds of meat each month, and in the wild, hunting takes up much of their time.

The range of Siberian tigers used to extend over much of China, Korea, and Siberia, but the destruction of their habitats due to the expansion of the human population into these areas has caused a drastic decrease in their numbers. Estimates now place their population at fewer than 200.

# Creating a Board Game

## Materials

- Make-Your-Own Gameboard (1 per student)
- Scissors, tape
- Colored pencils or markers
- Game pieces
- Calculators

## What Happens

Students design their own games based on the number line, play them with other students, and revise them. Their work focuses on:

- relating the direction of movement (left or right, up or down) to positive and negative numbers
- using net change to determine an end point

## Designing a Board Game

Distribute the Make-Your-Own Gameboard (2 sheets) to each student. The first sheet has spaces numbered from –6 to 5. The second sheet has empty spaces that students can use to extend their gameboard, writing in the numbers themselves.

Working individually or in pairs, students choose a theme for their game. They draw special instructions in some of the spaces to make players gain or lose something to get them closer to or farther from their goal.

If your class is involved in a special social studies, science, or literature unit, students may want to base their games on the same theme. Some students have used money as a theme for their games, others have used personal interests such as space travel or a sport, others have used ecological themes. For more ideas, see the **Teacher Note,** Themes for Board Games (p. 54).

Students may want to challenge their computation skills by using difficult numbers. For example, in a game about earning and spending money, some students included realistic prices such as $24.98 and $79.39. Other students have included doubling and halving among their bonuses and penalties. This is where calculators can be useful.

Students make a first draft of their games, including a brief set of instructions. Advise them not to spend too much time on the pictures, as they will be doing a final version after they've tested their games.

When students are ready, they try their games with classmates. As they play, they think of ways to revise the board and new rules that might make the game more enjoyable. In class and perhaps for homework, they revise their games based on feedback they receive.

They finally make finished gameboards, coloring and illustrating them to make them more attractive.

Students also write a more complete set of game instructions so that others could play the game without an oral explanation. You might provide time outside of math class for students to write the game instructions, to read and give feedback on each other's instructions, and to write a final version.

❖ **Tip for the Linguistically Diverse Classroom**  For this task, pair students with limited English proficiency and students who are proficient in English. After the partners agree on how to play their original games, English-proficient students can write the instructions. Their partners can add rebus pictures to the directions, making them more attractive as well as easier to understand.

## Trying Out the Games

As the unit ends, you may want to use one of the following options for creating a record of students' work on this unit.

■ Students look back through their folders or notebooks and write about what they learned in this unit, what they remember most, what was hard or easy for them. You might have students do this work during their writing time.

■ Students select one or two pieces of their work as their best work, and you also choose one or two pieces of their work, to be saved in a port-folio for the year. You might include students' written solutions to the assessments Six Changes and a Missing Start (p. 27) and Repeating Elevator Problem (p. 44), and any other assessment tasks from this unit. Students can create a separate page with brief comments describing each piece of work.

■ You may want to send a selection of work home for parents to see. Students write a cover letter describing their work in this unit. This work should be returned if you are keeping a portfolio of mathematics work for each student.

## Choosing Student Work to Save

# Sessions 2 and 3 Follow-Up

**Finishing at Home**   Students can finish writing their revised game instructions at home if there is not time in class.

**Sharing the Games**   Make arrangements for students to play their board games with students from another class. If you do this, you may want to preserve the gameboards, perhaps by laminating them or covering them with clear contact paper.

**Setting Up a Games Center**   Students may want to continue playing their own games and games they learned earlier in this unit. You might designate a certain area in the room where materials and directions for each game are available after this unit is completed.

Post a list of the available games and review the rules with students as needed. The center could include the Game of Many Changes, Pick Up Chips, Save the Siberian Tiger, and students' original games, as well as games from other units in the *Investigations* curriculum.

---

## Teacher Note

### Themes for Board Games

Students may base their board games on any theme that lends itself to players gradually getting closer to a goal. Some ideas are listed below:

■ Students choose a favorite sport. For example, in a game based on basketball, players aim for spaces where they make baskets and try to avoid spaces where they are penalized for committing fouls. For a gymnastics theme, players aim for spaces where they successfully complete a routine and avoid spaces where they lose their balance or make a move badly.

■ Students choose a favorite animal and pretend that the mother and her many babies have gotten separated. Throughout the game, the mother aims for spaces where the babies are located and avoids spaces where dangers are lurking.

■ Students choose another endangered animal and model a game after it.

■ Students choose a favorite destination for a travel game. They aim for spaces that move them along and avoid spaces that delay their arrival.

■ Students make up a secret message. Players aim for spaces where they can claim parts of the message and avoid spaces where they are prevented from doing this.

Almost any topic your students have been studying or are interested in could be used for this game: the adventures of a fictional character, events in the life of a historical figure, a local community project, and so on.

# Estimation and Number Sense

## Basic Activity

Students mentally estimate the answer to an arithmetic problem that they see displayed for about a minute. They discuss their estimates. Then they find a precise solution to the problem by using mental computation strategies.

Estimation and Number Sense provides opportunities for students to develop strategies for mental computation and for judging the reasonableness of the results of a computation done on paper or with a calculator. Students focus on:

■ looking at a problem as a whole

■ reordering or combining numbers within a problem for easier computation

■ looking at the largest part of each number first (looking at hundreds before tens, thousands before hundreds, and so forth)

## Materials

Calculators (for variation)

## Procedure

### Step 1. Present a problem on the chalkboard or overhead.   For example:

$$9 + 62 + 91 + 30$$

### Step 2. Allow about a minute for students to think about the problem.   In this time, students come up with the best estimate they can for the solution. This solution might be—but does not have to be—an exact answer. Students do not write anything down or use the calculator during this time.

### Step 3. Cover the problem and ask students to discuss what they know.   Ask questions like these: "What did you notice about the numbers in this problem? Did you estimate an answer? How did you make your estimate?"

Encourage all kinds of estimation statements and strategies. Some will be more general; others may be quite precise:

"It's definitely bigger than 100 because I saw a 90 and a 60."

"It has to be 192 because the 91 and the 9 make 100 and the 30 and the 62 make 92."

Be sure that you continue to encourage a variety of observations, especially the "more than, less than" statements, even if some students have solved it exactly.

### Step 4. Uncover the problem and continue the discussion.   Ask further: "What do you notice now? What do you think about your estimates? Do you want to change them? What are some mental strategies you can use to solve the problem exactly?"

## Variations

**Problems That Can Be Reordered**   Give problems like the following examples, in which grouping the numbers in particular ways can help solve the problem easily:

$$6 + 2 - 4 + 1 - 5 + 4 + 5 - 2$$

$$36 + 22 + 4 + 8$$

$$112 - 30 + 60 - 2$$

$$654 - 12 + 300 + 112$$

Encourage students to look at the problem as a whole before they start to solve it. Rather than using each number and operation in sequence, they see what numbers are easy to put together to give answers to part of the problem. Then they combine their partial results to solve the whole problem.

**Problems with Large Numbers**   Present problems that require students to "think from left to right" and to round numbers to "nice numbers" in order to come up with a good estimate. For example:

*Continued on next page*

$$
\begin{array}{r}
230 \\
343 \\
+\,692 \\
\hline
\end{array}
\qquad
\$\,3.15 \times 9
\qquad
\begin{array}{r}
\$5.13 \\
\$6.50 \\
+\ \ \$3.30 \\
\hline
\end{array}
$$

$$8 + 1200 + 130$$

Present problems in both horizontal and vertical formats. If the vertical format triggers a rote procedure of starting from the right and "carrying," encourage students to look at the numbers as a whole, and to think about the largest parts of the numbers first. Thus, for the problem 230 + 343 + 692, they might think first, "About how much is 692?—700." Then, thinking in terms of the largest part of the numbers first (hundreds), they might reason: "300 and 700 is a thousand, and 200 more is 1200, and then there's some extra, so I think it's a little over 1200."

**Fractions**   Pose problems using fractions and ask students to estimate the number of wholes the result is closest to. Start by posing problems such as 1/2 + 1/4 or 1/2 + 3/4, and ask, "Is the answer more than or less than one?" Eventually, you can include fractions with larger results and expand the question to "Is the answer closer to 0, 1, or 2?" Begin to include problems such as 5 × 1/4 and 3 × 1/8. Use fractions such as 9/4, 50/7, 100/26, or 63/20, and ask, "About how many wholes are in this fraction?"

**Is It Bigger or Smaller?**   Use any of the kinds of problems suggested above, but pose a question about the result to help students focus their estimation: "Is this bigger than 20? Is it smaller than $10.00? If I have $20.00, do I have enough to buy these four things?"

**Using the Calculator**   The calculator can be used to check results  Emphasize that it is easy to make mistakes on a calculator, and that many people who use calculators all the time often make mistakes. Sometimes you punch in the wrong key or the wrong operation. Sometimes you leave out a number by accident, or a key sticks on the calculator and doesn't register. However, people who are good at using the calculator always make a mental estimate so they can tell whether their result is reasonable.

Pose some problems like this one:

> I was adding 212, 357, and 436 on my calculator. The answer I got was 685. Was that a reasonable answer? Why do you think so?

Include problems in which the result is reasonable and problems in which it is not. When the answer is unreasonable, some students might be interested in figuring out what happened. For example, in the above case, 46 was accidentally pressed instead of 436.

### Related Homework Options

**Problems with Many Numbers**  Give one problem with many numbers that must be added and subtracted. Students show how they can reorder the numbers in the problem to make it easier to solve. They solve the problem using two different methods to double-check their solution. One way might be using the calculator. Here is an example of such a problem:

$$30 - 6 + 92 - 20 + 56 + 70 + 8$$

The following activities will help ensure that this unit is comprehensible to students who are acquiring English as a second language. The suggested approach is based on *The Natural Approach: Language Acquisition in the Classroom* by Stephen D. Krashen and Tracy D. Terrell (Alemany Press, 1983). The intent is for second-language learners to acquire new vocabulary in an active, meaningful context.

Note that *acquiring* a word is different from *learning* a word. Depending on their level of proficiency, students may be able to comprehend a word upon hearing it during an investigation, without being able to say it. Other students may be able to use the word orally, but not read or write it. The goal is to help students naturally acquire targeted vocabulary at their present level of proficiency.

We suggest using these activities just before the related investigations. The activities can also be led by English-proficient students.

## Investigation 1

*skyscraper, floor, ground level, elevator, button*

1. Show and identify a picture of one or more *skyscrapers*. With a marker, draw parallel, horizontal lines up one of the buildings. Explain that these are all the *floors* in this tall, tall building. Point to the floor level and to the surrounding land as you explain that this is referred to as the *ground floor,* or *ground level* in a building.

2. Draw some stairs on the board. Point to the drawing and ask if anyone would like to climb stairs to reach the top floor of a skyscraper.

3. Draw a quick sketch of an elevator. As you identify and point to it, pantomime pushing the *button,* waiting, getting inside, and moving up.

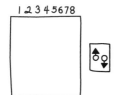

Ask students which they would rather use to get to the top of a skyscraper: stairs or an elevator.

4. Tell students to follow your actions as you take imaginary elevator rides up and down in a skyscraper.

   **We are at the ground floor [*point*], but we want to go to the sixth floor [*point*]. Push the elevator button [*push button on your sketch*] to go up. [*Pantomime going up six floors.*] Now we need to go to the third floor. [*Continue in this way.*]**

*starting, ending*

1. Write the following series of numbers on the board:

   12, 13, 14, 15, 16

   1, 2, 3, 4, 5, 6, 7

   35, 36, 37, 38, 39, 40, 41

   Point out that each set of numbers has a different starting and ending point from the rest. Identify each starting and ending number.

2. Write three more series of numbers on the board. Ask students to stand up whenever you point to a starting number, and to sit down whenever you point to an ending number. Also give students a chance to be the "pointer."

## Investigations 2–3

*gain, lose, opposite*

1. Give one girl and one boy 10 chips each. Toss a die, and give the girl the number of chips shown on the die. Explain that the girl gains a chip for each dot.

2. Now explain that you will do the opposite with the boy. Toss the die again, and take away the number of chips shown. Explain that the boy loses a chip for each dot.

3. Collect the chips and put them in a pile. Tell the students to smile and cheer if the pile gains chips, and to look sad if the pile loses chips. Toss the die again and randomly add or take away the corresponding number of chips.

*Continued on next page*

4. Challenge students to demonstrate comprehension of these targeted words by varying the activity. Choose students to do what you say, and then do the opposite.

Thus: **The pile gains four chips.** [*The student adds four chips.*]
**What's the opposite?** [*The student takes away four chips.*]

## Investigation 3

*tiger, cubs, habitat, wolf, boars, deer, destroy, hunting*

1. Show pictures of these wild animals in their native habitat: tiger with *cubs, fox, wolf, boar, deer.* Identify each as you explain that they are living in nature, or in the wild, not in a zoo. Explain that this is the animal's *habitat.*

2. Make a few sketches (for example, a fire, or people and buildings) to show ways these animals' habitat could be destroyed.

3. Ask students to compare the animals by responding to questions that require only one-word responses.

   **Which is bigger, a fox or a tiger?**

   **Which has a longer tail, a deer or a fox?**

   **Who has cubs, a deer or a tiger?**

4. Pantomime a tiger as you explain that this animal is hunting for food. Then create yes-or-no questions about which animal is the hunter and which the prey.

   **Would a tiger hunt a deer?**

   **Would a wolf hunt a deer?**

   **Would a deer hunt a wolf?**

   **Would a wolf hunt a tiger?**

   **Would a tiger hunt a boar?**

# Blackline Masters

Family Letter    60

_____ , 20 ____

# Dear Family,

Our class is starting a new math unit called *Up and Down the Number Line.* In this unit, your child will start to work with positive numbers (like +1, +2) and negative numbers (like –1, –2). We'll put together combinations of positive and negative numbers, which we'll call changes, to see what results we get. Most of the work is done through games, some of which involve imaginary trips in an elevator, up and down a skyscraper.

For example, one challenging problem that your child might do is this:

> I got on the elevator at some floor in my building. I moved up two floors, then down three floors, and I ended up on the fifth floor. What floor did I start on?

It takes some thinking to solve this. We'll do many problems like this in class, and the children will invent some of their own problems about elevator trips. Sometimes your child will bring these games home to teach to you. As you play together, talk with your child about his or her strategies for thinking about and keeping track of the changes. You and your child should feel free to invent your own problems as you play.

In about two weeks, the class will be making graphs of elevator trips. To prepare for this, they will be looking at graphs from newspapers and other sources that show things that change over time, such as temperatures, heights, or population. If you can, please help your child find one or two graphs to bring to school.

Using numbers to describe how something changes is a very important part of mathematics. Thinking about ups and downs helps children learn how to describe mathematical changes. In the future, they'll use these skills in both science and math as they describe and graph how things change.

Sincerely,

# Net Change from Start to Finish

| Starting Floor | Ending Floor | Net Change |
|---|---|---|
|  |  |  |
|  |  |  |
|  |  |  |
|  |  |  |
|  |  |  |
|  |  |  |
|  |  |  |
|  |  |  |
|  |  |  |
|  |  |  |
|  |  |  |

| Starting Floor | Ending Floor | Net Change |
|---|---|---|
|  |  |  |
|  |  |  |
|  |  |  |
|  |  |  |
|  |  |  |
|  |  |  |
|  |  |  |
|  |  |  |
|  |  |  |
|  |  |  |
|  |  |  |

# Net Change with Many Changes

| Net Change | Changes |
|---|---|
|  |  |
|  |  |
|  |  |
|  |  |
|  |  |
|  |  |
|  |  |
|  |  |
|  |  |
|  |  |

| Net Change | Changes |
|---|---|
|  |  |
|  |  |
|  |  |
|  |  | 62 |
|  |  |
|  |  |
|  |  |
|  |  |
|  |  |
|  |  |

*Investigation 1 • Sessions 3–4*
*Up and Down the Number Line*

# How to Play the Game of Many Changes

**Materials**
Net Change Cards (one set)
Changes Cards (one set for each player)
Skyscraper, game piece for each player

**Players:** 2 to 4

**How to Play**
1. Turn your set of Changes Cards face down in front of you. Place the Net Change Cards face down in the center.

2. Take seven Changes Cards from your set and spread these face up in front of you. (All players do this.)

3. Turn over the top Net Change Card to begin the round. Use as many of your seven Changes Cards as possible to make the net change shown on the Net Change Card. You may use your skyscraper and game piece to test your set of changes.

4. Players check each other's sets of changes to see if they work. Use Student Sheet 2 to record the net change and the changes you make in each round.

5. For each round, start with seven new Changes Cards. Turn up another Net Change Card to begin the round.

**Variation**
Start by picking only five Changes Cards to make the net change shown. After you have used as many of the five changes as you can, turn your pack of Changes Cards face up and choose two more cards. The goal is to use all seven of your cards.

# Many Changes to Make +2

Pick any changes you want from one whole deck of Changes Cards. Make the longest set of changes that gives you a net change of +2.

Then answer these questions:

What cards did you use?

_____

_____

What card or cards did you *not* use?

_____

_____

Explain why the cards you did not use would not work to make a net change of +2.

_____

_____

_____

_____

_____

# Mixed-Up Changes

Reorder the sequence of changes below so that it is easy to figure out the net change. Show and explain your strategy.

+13 −55 +17 +70 −27 −15

Net Change_____

Now write a new set of five or six changes that has a large net change. First, write the changes in a mixed-up order that makes it difficult to figure out the net change. Second, reorder the sequence to make it easy to figure out the net change.

Net Change_____

# Missing Information Problems

| Starting Floor | Changes | Ending Floor |
|---|---|---|
|  |  |  |
|  |  |  |
|  |  |  |
|  |  |  |
|  |  |  |
|  |  |  |

This is who invented the problems:

_____    _____

This is who solved the problems:

_____    _____

A strategy that worked for us was:

_____

_____

_____

_____

# Six Changes and a Missing Start

1.  You want to ride around in the elevator. You push
    six change buttons to get from floor 4 to floor 3.
    Name six buttons that you could push.

    _____  _____  _____  _____  _____  _____

    List some other combinations of six buttons that
    would work.

    _____  _____  _____  _____  _____  _____

    _____  _____  _____  _____  _____  _____

    _____  _____  _____  _____  _____  _____

2.  You push three change buttons on the elevator:

    $$-3 \quad +2 \quad -1$$

    You end at floor 4. Where did you start? _____

    Explain how you found the starting place.

    _____

    _____

    _____

    _____

# Pick Up Chips

| Name | Start | Order of Changes | Number of Chips |
|------|-------|------------------|-----------------|
|      |       |                  |                 |
|      |       |                  |                 |
|      |       |                  |                 |
|      |       |                  |                 |
|      |       |                  |                 |
|      |       |                  |                 |
|      |       |                  |                 |
|      |       |                  |                 |
|      |       |                  |                 |
|      |       |                  |                 |
|      |       |                  |                 |
|      |       |                  |                 |
|      |       |                  |                 |
|      |       |                  |                 |
|      |       |                  |                 |
|      |       |                  |                 |

# How to Play Pick Up Chips

**Materials** (for each player)
Skyscraper
10 chips
Set of Changes Cards
Pick Up Chips recording chart (Student Sheet 8)

**Players:** any number, playing as individuals or pairs

**How to Play**
1. Place your skyscraper up and down in front of you. Place your chips on any ten floors in a row.

2. One player draws four Changes Cards. Place them face up. The other players find the same cards in their decks and place them face up in front of them.

3. Each elevator starts at 0. The Changes Cards tell where the elevator will go after that. Try to arrange your cards so the elevator stops on as many different floors as possible.

4. Pick up the chip at the starting floor and at each floor you visit. The goal is to pick up as many chips as possible.

5. After each round, write everyone's results on the Pick Up Chips recording sheet.

6. For a new round, put all the chips back on your skyscraper. Take turns choosing a new set of four Changes Cards.

**Variation**
Arrange the Changes Cards to stop on as *few* different floors as possible.

Cut along the dotted lines. Tape the strips together
with 0 in the middle.

|  |  |
|---|---|
|  | **0** |
|  | **1** |
| **4** | **2** |
| **3** | **3** |
| **2** |  |
| **1** |  |

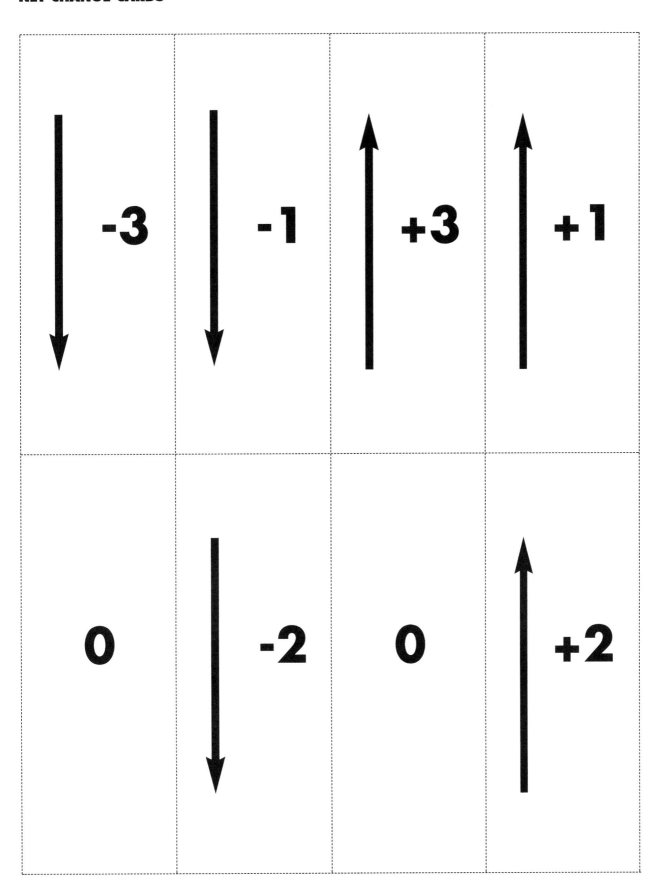

# Change-Over-Time Graphs

Look in newspapers, books, magazines, and other sources for graphs that show something changing over time. For example, you might find graphs of temperatures, speeds, ages, or weights.

I found a graph about _____

_____.

This is where I found it: _____

_____.

I found a graph about _____

_____.

This is where I found it: _____

_____.

I found a graph about _____

_____.

This is where I found it: _____

_____.

# Plus and Minus Graphs

| | |
|---|---|
| **1.**  − − + + + | |
| **2.**  + + 0 0 − | |
| **3.**  + + − − − | |
| **4.**  0 − + + + | |
| **5.**  + + − − + | |
| **6.**  − + + + − | |

# Repeating Elevator Problem

Here is a graph of a broken elevator trip. This elevator repeats the same set of changes over and over.
The elevator has gone through the set of changes twice.

1. Repeat the same set of changes one more time on the graph.

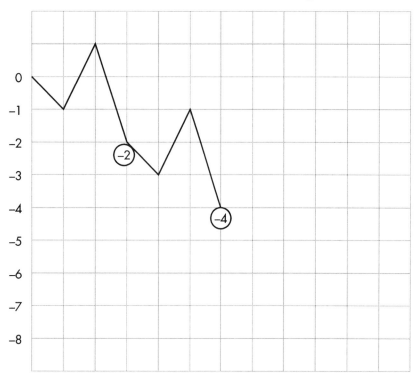

2. What is the set of changes that the elevator keeps repeating?

_____

3. What is the net change of one set of the changes on the graph?

_____

4. Describe what happens to the elevator if it keeps repeating the pattern forever.

_____

_____

_____

# Net Change on a Graph

Figure out the net change for each graph in two different ways. Show your solutions on the back of this sheet.

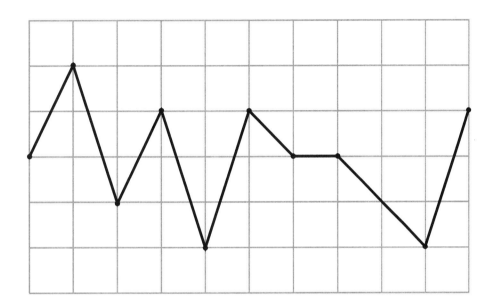

Net = _____

Net = _____

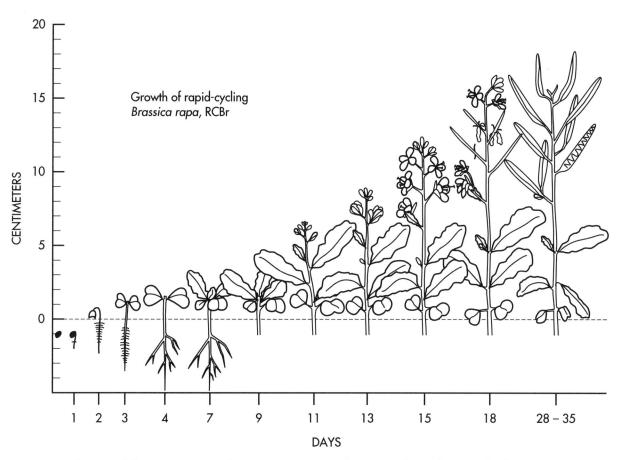

Growth of rapid-cycling
*Brassica rapa, RCBr*

CENTIMETERS

DAYS

Based on a graph from Wisconsin Fast Plants, ©1993 Wisconsin Alumni Research Foundation. Used with permission.

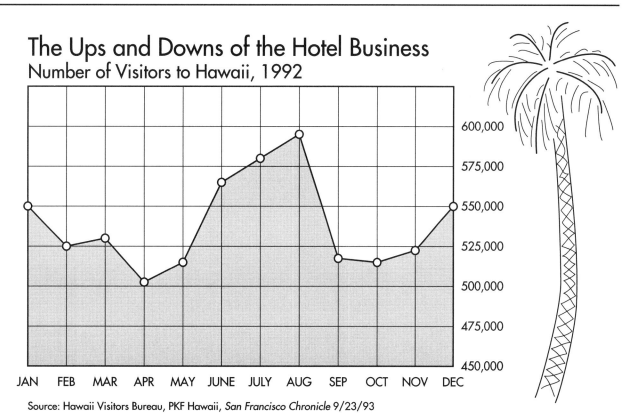

# The Ups and Downs of the Hotel Business
## Number of Visitors to Hawaii, 1992

Source: Hawaii Visitors Bureau, PKF Hawaii, *San Francisco Chronicle* 9/23/93

**77**

*Investigation 2 • Resource*
*Up and Down the Number Line*

# REPEATING ELEVATOR GRAPHS

**A.**

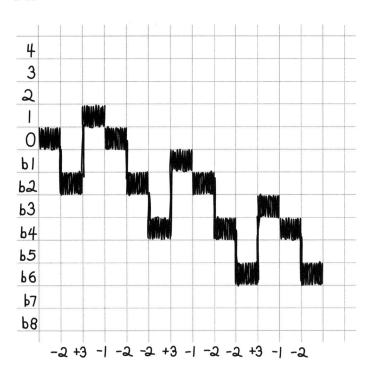

-2  +3  -1  -2  -2  +3  -1  -2  -2  +3  -1  -2

**B.**

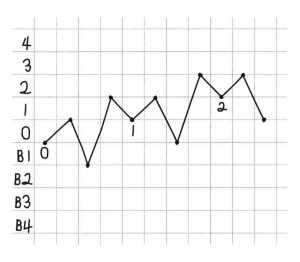

**C.**

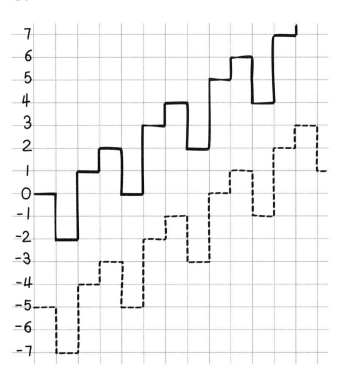

**D.**

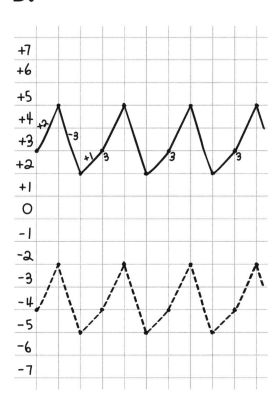

# SMALL PLUS AND MINUS CARDS

| **TOP** | **TOP** |
|---|---|
| − − + + + | + + 0 0 − |
| **TOP** | **TOP** |
| + + − − − | 0 − + + + |
| **TOP** | **TOP** |
| + + − − + | − + + + − |

**TOP**

$$-\quad-\quad+\quad+\quad+$$

**TOP**

$$+\quad+\quad 0\quad 0\quad -$$

**TOP**

$$+\quad+\quad-\quad-\quad-$$

**TOP**

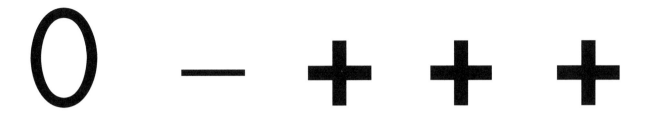

**TOP**

**TOP**

*Investigation 2 • Resource*
*Up and Down the Number Line*

# How to Play Save the Siberian Tiger

**Materials**
Siberian Tiger Gameboard
A game piece for each player
Changes Cards (one set for each player)
Tiger Cards (one or two sets)

1 tiger

**Players:** 2 or 3

**How to Play**
1. Each player starts with six Changes Cards spread face up: –3, –2, –1, +1, +2, +3. These are the CHOICE cards. All players mix the rest of their Changes Cards. Place them in a stack face down. These are the CHANCE cards. Place the Tiger Cards in a Tiger Bank.

2. Players take turns. Begin with your game piece on START. For each turn, draw two CHANCE cards. Your move is the net change of the two cards. Move left with a negative number, right with a positive number. A net change of 0 returns you to the same square.

   On any turn, you may also use a CHOICE card. Your move is then the net change of the three cards.

   Use each card only once. Put used cards in a discard pile.

3. With each turn, you may GAIN tigers from the Tiger Bank. If you LOSE tigers, return them to the bank. Your goal is to save the most tigers.

4. If you are close to one end of the board and can't move with your two CHANCE cards, then use only a CHOICE card for that move. If you can't use a CHOICE card, skip a turn.

5. Play ends when there are no more CHANCE cards. Count to see who has saved the most tigers.

**SAVE THE SIBERIAN TIGER GAMEBOARD** (page 1 of 2)

Cut page 1 and page 2 along the dotted lines. Tape the strips together from –11 to 11 with 0 in the middle.

| –11 | –10 | –9 | –8 | –7 | –6 |
|---|---|---|---|---|---|
| Law passed: No tiger hunting. | Forest burned. | Pollution downstream. No salmon. | Tigers captured for zoos. | Tiger habitat destroyed. | Exceptionally cold winter. |
| *Double number of tigers.* | *Lose 48 tigers.* | *Lose 9 tigers.* | *Lose 6 tigers.* | *Cut number of tigers in half.* | *Lose 23 tigers.* |

| –5 | –4 | –3 | –2 | –1 | 0 |
|---|---|---|---|---|---|
| Law passed to protect tiger habitat. | Tiger range restricted. | Drought. | Human community built. | Tiger cubs born. | START |
| *Gain 75 tigers.* | *Go back to 0. Collect no new tigers.* | *Lose 17 tigers.* | *Lose 61 tigers.* | *Gain 23 tigers.* | |

© Pearson Education, Inc.

**83**

*Investigation 3 • Resource*
*Up and Down the Number Line*

| 1 | 2 | 3 | 4 | 5 | 6 |
|---|---|---|---|---|---|
| Tigers kill deer. | Road built through territory. | Dry year for grass. No elk. | Tiger cubs born. | Wolves and foxes hunted by humans. | Blizzard. |
| *Gain 55 tigers.* | *Lose 36 tigers.* | *Lose 14 tigers.* | *Gain 20 tigers.* | *Lose 8 tigers.* | *Lose 15 tigers.* |

| 7 | 8 | 9 | 10 | 11 |
|---|---|---|---|---|
| Tigers killed by poachers. | Tigers kill wild boars. | Tiger range restricted. | Town expanded. | Law passed: No tiger hunting. |
| *Lose 18 tigers.* | *Gain 41 tigers.* | *Go back to 0. Collect no new tigers.* | *Lose 9 tigers.* | *Gain 100 tigers.* |

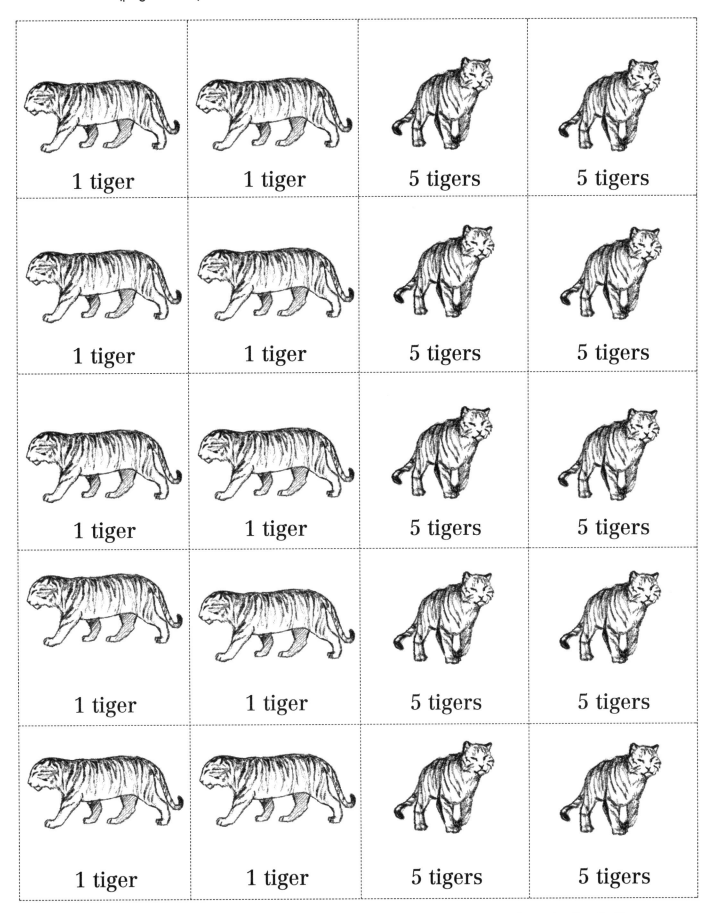

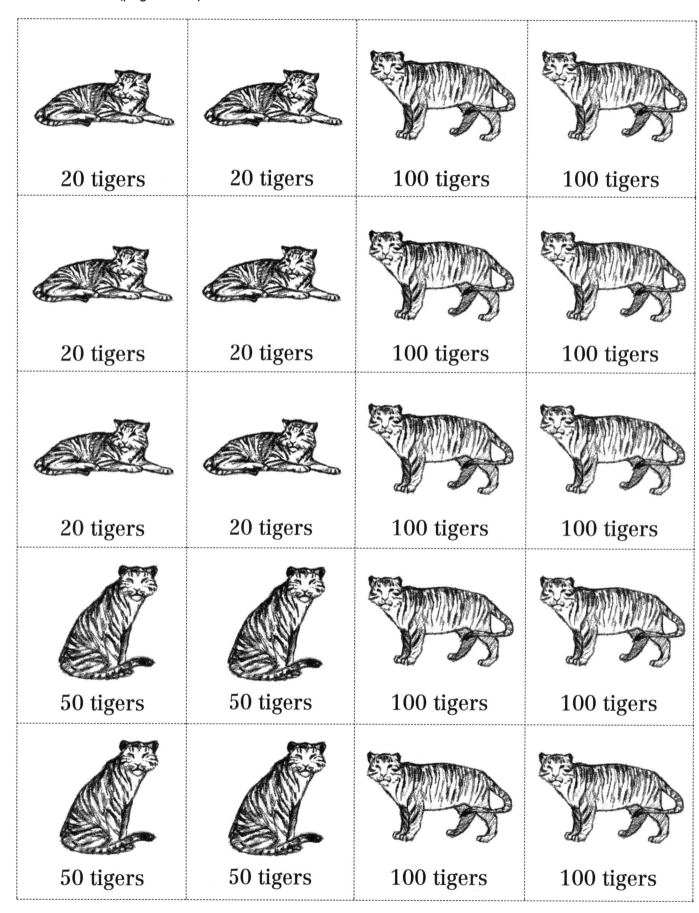

20 tigers | 20 tigers | 100 tigers | 100 tigers

20 tigers | 20 tigers | 100 tigers | 100 tigers

20 tigers | 20 tigers | 100 tigers | 100 tigers

50 tigers | 50 tigers | 100 tigers | 100 tigers

50 tigers | 50 tigers | 100 tigers | 100 tigers

*Investigation 3 • Resource*
*Up and Down the Number Line*

Cut along the dotted lines. Tape the strips together with 0 in the middle.

| –6 | –5 | –4 | –3 | –2 | –1 |
|----|----|----|----|----|----|
|    |    |    |    |    |    |

| 0 | 1 | 2 | 3 | 4 | 5 |
|---|---|---|---|---|---|
|   |   |   |   |   |   |

*Investigation 3 • Resource*
*Up and Down the Number Line*

**MAKE-YOUR-OWN GAMEBOARD** (page 2 of 2)

Cut along the dotted lines. Tape one strip to each end of the long strip you made from page 1.

| | | | |
|---|---|---|---|
| **-3** | **-2** | **-1** | **0** |
| **+1** | **+2** | **+3** | **-3** |
| **-2** | **-1** | **0** | **+1** |
| **+2** | **+3** | **-3** | **-2** |
| **-1** | **+1** | **+2** | **+3** |

*Unit Resource*
*Up and Down the Number Line*

# Practice Pages

This optional section provides homework ideas for teachers who want or need to give more homework than is assigned to accompany the activities in this unit. The problems included here provide additional practice in learning about number relationships and in solving computation and number problems. For number units, you may want to use some of these if your students need more work in these areas or if you want to assign daily homework. For other units, you can use these problems so that students can continue to work on developing number and computation sense while they are focusing on other mathematical content in class. We recommend that you introduce activities in class before assigning related problems for homework.

**The Arranging Chairs Puzzle**   This activity is introduced in the unit *Things That Come in Groups*. If your students are familiar with the activity, you can simply send home the directions so that students can play at home. If your students have not done this activity before, introduce it in class and have students do it once or twice before sending it home. Early in the year, ask students to work with numbers such as 15, 18, and 24. Later in the year, as they become ready to work with larger numbers, they can try numbers such as 32, 42, or 50. You might have students do this activity two times for homework in this unit.

**Doubles and Halves**   This type of problem is introduced in the unit *Mathematical Thinking at Grade 3*. Here you are provided three of these problems for student homework. You can make up other problems in this format, using numbers that are appropriate for your students. Students record their strategies for solving the problems, using numbers, words, or pictures.

**How Many Legs?**   This type of problem is introduced in the unit *Things That Come in Groups*. Provided here are three such problems for student homework. You can make up other problems in this format, using numbers that are appropriate for your students. Students record their strategies for solving the problems, using numbers, words, or pictures.

# The Arranging Chairs Puzzle

## What You Will Need

30 small objects to use as chairs (for example, cubes, blocks, tiles, chips, pennies, buttons)

## What to Do

1. Choose a number greater than 30.

2. Figure out all the ways you can arrange that many chairs. Each row must have the same number of chairs. Your arrangements will make rectangles of different sizes.

3. Write down the dimensions of each rectangle you make.

4. Choose another number and start again. Be sure to make a new list of dimensions for each new number.

**Example**
All the ways to arrange 12 chairs

**Dimensions**
1 by 12
12 by 1
2 by 6
6 by 2
3 by 4
4 by 3

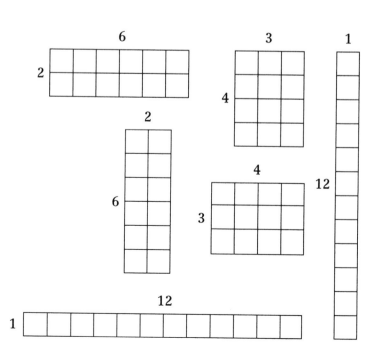

# Practice Page A

There are 78 beans in a bag. You are to split them evenly with a classmate. How many beans will each of you get?

Show how you solved this problem. You can use numbers, words, or pictures.

## Practice Page B

The dentist has 110 toothbrushes. He wants to put the same number of toothbrushes in each of two rooms. How many toothbrushes will he have in each room?

Show how you solved this problem. You can use numbers, words, or pictures.

## **Practice Page C**

An artist has 68 sheets of construction paper in one pile. Another pile has the same number of sheets. How many sheets of construction paper does the artist have?

Show how you solved this problem. You can use numbers, words, or pictures.

## **Practice Page D**

Show how you solved each problem. You can use numbers, words, or pictures.

A skateboard has 4 wheels.

How many wheels do 2 skateboards have?

How many wheels do 8 skateboards have?

How many wheels do 16 skateboards have?

## Practice Page E

We saw 4 insects, 3 elephants, and 5 people on our trip. Insects have 6 legs, and elephants have 4 legs. How many legs did we see?

Show how you solved the problem. You can use numbers, words, or pictures.

## Practice Page F

We saw 10 spiders and 5 mice in the field near our house. Spiders have 8 legs, and mice have 4 legs. How many legs did we see?

Show how you solved the problem. You can use numbers, words, or pictures.